Trying to See Round Corners

Trying to See
Round Corners

Reg Morris

Matador
9 Priory Business Park,
Wistow Road, Kibworth Beauchamp,
Leicestershire. LE8 0RX
Tel: 0116 279 2299
Email: books@troubador.co.uk
Web: www.troubador.co.uk/matador
Twitter: @matadorbooks

ISBN 978 1800463 271

British Library Cataloguing in Publication Data.
A catalogue record for this book is available from the British Library.

Printed and bound in Great Britain by 4edge Limited
Typeset in 10pt Gill Sans MT by Troubador Publishing Ltd, Leicester, UK

Matador is an imprint of Troubador Publishing Ltd

With fondest love to Willie,
whose worth is way beyond words.

Edited by Valerie McMahon

This collection of day-to-day episodes and conspiring challenges actually took place within Midlands local authority social services departments during the late twentieth century. The names of those concerned, however, who are variously seen as victims, bystanders or other players – have been changed to preserve their anonymity.

Reg Morris, 2020

CONTENTS

ONE

Sorts of rough and tumble

WHAT A WAY TO *spend Saturday morning*, Colin Millwood thought to himself. To make matters worse, if ever they could be, this was a day his kids had been looking forward to visiting the skatepark. Their mum would have to try to do that now though, sometime later, once she'd dealt with other things. *So be it*, Colin thought. There was really no way round it. They would all just have to grin and bear it. He was, after all, the senior social worker for this child.

The consultant paediatrician had unsurprisingly asked to speak to the social worker. There was no way that Colin could expect junior social worker Emmie Quayle to forsake the Saturday morning of the already hectic week she'd had with the family concerned. Someone who not only knew about the child, but who also had some decision-making authority, had to step up to the mark. Agreeing next steps was now a priority. That couldn't be left to others, especially duty social workers unfamiliar with the case, on a likely hectic weekend rota.

The consultant would be well aware that this was not little Stephanie Finch's first trip to hospital. Three or four previous occasions in recent weeks had the A&E department cataloguing just how accident-prone this active four-year-old happened to be. Her mum, Wendy, was almost on first-name terms with their staff. This was incredibly yet another instance of Stephanie sustaining more bumps and bruises. On this occasion, however, these had been seen by the social worker on a routine visit. It had of course prompted another well-trodden trip to hospital late on Friday afternoon.

This had understandably led to the child being admitted for observation and further tests. Certain questions would inevitably arise about the implications of even minor repetitive injuries upon the welfare of any four-year-old child. For her part though, Stephanie had been neither able nor keen to say how she had sustained bumps and bruises in this way.

Arriving at ward twenty-four, Colin explained to the staff nurse that he was due to meet with the consultant, Dr Corke, though no particular appointment time had been arranged. He declined the offer of tea, mainly in the interests of a busy staff team who clearly had plenty to do. This was despite much of the direct care of children on paediatric wards being provided by attentive parents. While Wendy Finch was not among them that morning, she was expected later, as she had another child at home, six-year old Cheryl.

As he patiently awaited the arrival of the consultant, Colin amiably joined other adults, mainly parents, in occupying some of the more active children. This variously took place around a popular four-legged sandpit, or otherwise amid an impressive abundance of larger toys donated by charitable organisations. Time must have effortlessly drifted by in this way before Colin was surprised to hear the outer corridor echoing with sounds of metal containers in transit. He realised it must be approaching lunchtime.

His heart sank at the thought of all the time that this appeared to be taking. He wondered if his own kids had actually made it to the skatepark. No matter, he could only grin and bear it. Finding himself conveniently seated at the lunch table near to Stephanie, he managed to include the child – rather than actively engage her – in occasional snippets of conversation. This largely took account of easy openings along the lines of, "What have you been playing with today?" and "What's your favourite game, or toy?" Since they hadn't met before, he purposely avoided, at this early stage, the more pressing question of why she was in hospital.

She responded confidently enough, though it caused him to wonder how limited her speech might be for a four year-old. "Will you be seeing Mummy today, Stephanie?" he asked kindly. She didn't reply, since she was evidently more interested in what she was eating by then, contentedly swinging her legs back and forth from the high seat of her chair.

"I don't want ter go 'ome, Mister," she said passively,

still swinging her legs and without looking up from the more appealing plate in front of her.

"Ooh, why ever not, Stephanie?" Colin asked.

"I like it 'ere," she replied, moving her head exaggeratedly from side to side with a happy smile. Staff had remarked how she had not appeared to be at all upset at being in hospital.

Their promising little chat was then forestalled by a member of nursing staff announcing that Dr Corke had arrived. As Colin made his way earnestly to meet the consultant, he wondered what line the doctor might be inclined to take with social workers. Medical consultants, in his experience, could sometimes be seen to assume superior airs and graces in these sorts of exchanges. As it happened, however, he need not have worried – Dr Corke was extremely polite and personable.

He began by asking Colin about the background of a child he had only recently met. He knew that she had previously been seen only fleetingly by other medical staff and seldom by paediatricians. Colin summarised an outline of Emmie's contact over the previous month or so with this single-parent family. Wendy Finch appeared to be someone under a degree of stress, as she tried her best to cope with the not untypical demands of two young children.

"Our focus has therefore been largely one of general support," he said, "especially through this series of bruising episodes. We have scrupulously followed appropriate guidance on each occasion. This has included the child being referred for successive medical opinions, mainly in eliminating any possibility of non-accidental injury."

"Was the family already known to you?" Dr Corke asked.

"Not exactly," Colin replied. "That said though, low-level concern had been expressed for Stephanie's elder sister, Cheryl, when the family lived in another locality, before Stephanie was born. Beyond that, Wendy had herself been a young person in local authority care."

"Oh," said Dr Corke. "Why was that?"

"She was committed to care by the juvenile court," Colin explained, "following intermittent episodes of, quite frankly, minor offending. While reference had also been made to difficulties that Wendy may have had with her own mother around that time, I'm afraid to say that we have been unable to find the file relating to them. A number of extended-family teenage Finches have also been known to social workers at various times for petty offending.

"Our first acquaintance locally with Stephanie was triggered by her headteacher, early in the new year. Nursery staff had discovered nasty bruising to her upper thigh. The child appeared to be in some discomfort and the head accordingly reported it to social services, particularly when the mother was unable to offer any explanation. You will of course be familiar with the sequel."

"Did you have any suspicions about it?" the consultant asked.

"Well no," Colin replied, "not really. The main doubt remained around the lack of any explanation by mother or child. On that basis alone, we arranged for her to be seen in A&E, but primarily to explore the prospect of any other injuries, accidental or otherwise."

"Hmm… it was said to have been the result of the child jumping from one bed to another in the children's bedroom," Dr Corke observed, gazing casually over his notes.

"So we gathered subsequently," Colin said. "That was certainly not mentioned initially."

"Anything since?" Dr Corke mused.

"Not really," said Colin. "It's been largely seen, as I've said, as a straightforward matter of family support. We would have closed the case earlier had it not been for those subsequent bumps and bruises that you're aware of. Having said that, some social work visits have coincided with other family members being present with their children. The social worker has remarked, more than once, how the children's play-fighting has been… well… excessive, and the adults have hardly taken any notice. It has every indication of being a rough-and-tumble sort of household.

"Beyond that, the social worker has recognised the growing family's limited space in a ground-floor flat. Consequently, representation has been made to Housing in supporting Wendy's application for a transfer – not just to bigger accommodation, but somewhat closer to wider family."

"Not the rough-and-tumble brigade, then?" Dr Corke mused with a smile.

"Hopefully not," returned Colin. "Despite all of that, the social worker's bottom line is one of Wendy appearing to genuinely love her kids. There has been no evidence of neglect beyond the context of limited income. Although,

Mum sometimes describes Cheryl's behaviour as 'difficult'. The social worker has tended to attribute that to elements of sibling rivalry and has advised accordingly."

"What about Dad? Does he have any contact?" Dr Corke asked.

"I have to confess," Colin admitted, "I don't know. I would need to ask my colleague about that," he added, feeling somewhat ashamed at this elementary gap in basic knowledge of the case.

This was particularly galling for Colin, who inwardly agonised over this unforgivable oversight. It was he, of all people, who would frequently remind his team how professional literature condemned social work's neglect of the part played by fathers in family life. Such casual indifference sometimes unwittingly consigned men to fade anonymously from view, with unfortunate or even tragic consequences. It also extended, he would point out, to social workers acquiring a similarly tarnished reputation for dwelling excessively on *mother-blame*. "It's fundamental information-gathering!" he would exclaim to his colleagues.

"No matter," said the consultant dismissively, "this hospital visit for Stephanie appears to be of little difference from others. There are no significant injuries to be seen, nothing at all in suspicious areas, and the child is generally in good physical health."

"Have you seen Mum?" Colin asked.

"No, I haven't," Dr Corke replied, "but my registrar has. Staff report that mother and child have interacted fairly well. So," he added, pursing his lips, "as things stand she doesn't really need to be in hospital, unless of course you were to have any pressing concerns that need to be considered."

"Well, no, not really," Colin replied, still inwardly seething over his own shortcomings. Moreover, his noble gesture of meeting the consultant over a weekend was turning into a dismal anti-climax. He began to feel that he might have been better employed at the skatepark after all. "We'll remain involved until the housing transfer takes place," he added. "Mum – Wendy – will certainly benefit from being closer to more supportive relatives and their transfer to Greenways is likely to be confirmed any time now."

"Okay then," said Dr Corke. "Sounds promising, especially if it brings a marked reduction in rough and tumble." Colin smiled, short of any smart answer. "I'll let the staff nurse know that the child is for discharge and she can be taken home as soon as those arrangements are made. Perhaps you can liaise with staff nurse about it? If you do happen, however, to have any further concerns of this nature for this child," the consultant added, "by all means get directly back to me rather than trying to negotiate the more convoluted A&E route."

"Oh, that's really helpful, Dr Corke," Colin gratefully replied. "I certainly will." They shook hands before Colin went in search of Stephanie again.

He soon spotted her, playing in the sandpit with the other kids, or rather, alongside them. Stephanie was commenting loudly on important items monopolising her attention as she filled buckets of sand. Colin observed the children quietly, at some distance, as they occupied themselves contentedly. He was then shaken from his own thoughts by the staff nurse approaching him with a broad smile. The two of them casually exchanged information about Stephanie and her imminent discharge. It would coincide, as Colin explained, with her mum's anticipated arrival on the ward and his offering to take them home.

Eventually, as parents continued to congregate intermittently in and around the sandpit to occupy their offspring, a young woman confidently approached the gathering. This caused Stephanie's eyes to light up excitedly. It was obviously her mum, who Colin had never met before.

He introduced himself politely. Wendy looked up at him quickly, with a frown, before asking curtly, "What are you doin' 'ere then?"

"The doctor asked to speak to the social worker," he said. "I came here on my colleague Emmie's behalf, since it's Saturday, to explain how Emmie has remained in touch with you and Stephanie as you look forward to moving to Greenways. I then hung on for you to give you a lift home."

"She's *Stephie* ter them as know 'er," Wendy replied, with uninhibited feeling. "I'll be all right gettin' 'ome. I'll ring me sister."

"I really don't mind running you home," Colin said, trying to be helpful.

"It's all right," Wendy replied emphatically. "I'll be okay."

"Fair enough then," he said, yielding to this unwavering intent. "Emmie will be in touch with you sometime next week then, Wendy." She said nothing in reply, neither did

Stephanie. They were each far too engrossed with the sandpit as he bade them farewell.

Colin immediately turned his mind towards getting back to his own family. He was keen to find ways of seriously making amends for their disrupted weekend. Leaving the main area of the ward, however, he encountered Dr Corke again, emerging from the ward office. "Oh, hello again, Mr Millwood," he exclaimed. "Have you been able to make contact with the child's mother yet?"

"Well, I have for what it was worth," he replied. "She gave every indication of not being entirely over the moon to see me. I'll just put that down to what I am, rather than taking it too personally."

"Did she say anything?" the consultant asked.

"Not really," Colin replied with a shrug, "for whatever reason. I think that *taciturn* might best describe her response."

Dr Corke raised his eyebrows with a smile. "Hmm… someone once said," he reflected, "that a mother is only ever as happy as her least happy child." And the two of them each went on their way.

Colin tried quickly to unpick Dr Corke's train of thought before dismissing it. He pressed on regardless to begin to regain some measure of credibility with his own family. While a trip to Pizza Palace went some way to restore just desserts, his kids subsequently seized upon the even more gratifying follow-up of ten-pin bowling to round things off. This was at last seen as a fair reward.

It was not until their kids were in bed that Colin shared with his wife, Helen, some of the ups and downs of what had felt like his earlier rocky ride with family Finch, albeit anonymously portrayed. "The bottom line is," he said, not for the first time, "that Mother appears in many ways to really care about her kids."

"That's sometimes not enough," Helen unwaveringly replied. "Caring is very much a matter of what you do, as well as what you may feel, and even more, of course, of what you may ever be inclined to say."

"Hmm... I suppose so," was all that Colin could utter at the end of a trying day. It then turned into an equally unsettled night. It was not a matter of his necessarily feeling troubled by the events of that day, but rather of his experiencing feelings of uncertainty about what family life was really like for the Finches. His tossing and turning was, at length, suddenly interrupted by the shrill ringing of the telephone downstairs.

Colin lumbered almost unsteadily down the staircase, wondering whatever time it could be. Not even his kids had yet stirred, which must have said something for the ungodliness of the hour. "Colin Millwood?" said a vibrant voice at the other end of the line.

"Ye-es," replied Colin, a trifle puzzled and still half asleep.

"Yvonne Glendenning here, Emergency Duty Team." It was a name that meant nothing to Colin. "I'm ringing about a child named Stephanie Finch," the voice announced in a continuingly detached tone.

"Yes?" said Colin, "I was with her for much of yesterday."

"Well," said the voice from the other end of the phone, "I have been asked to inform you that she has been readmitted to hospital in the early hours and is currently in intensive care. The duty consultant, Dr Purcell, describes her condition as moribund. Mother has been arrested and is in custody. The child's sibling is with her maternal grandmother. I don't think there is anything for us to do right now," the voice added with a hint of compassion. "I just needed to let you know."

Colin felt sick. Weak at the knees, he sank down onto the cold tiled floor of his hallway, receiver in hand. "Okay," he uttered. "I'll need to get over there anyway. I'll be on ward twenty-four should you need to get hold of me."

"We will willingly attend if you think there is anything we might be able to do," Yvonne said, now much more considerately.

"Thanks anyway, Yvonne," he replied, "but whatever may need doing by us today will have to be down to me."

"Who on earth was it at this hour?" Helen queried on Colin's morose return upstairs. "Oh no, Colin," she then gasped when he told her the news. Without washing or showering, he dressed in a fractious daze before making his way robotically back to the hospital.

His unannounced arrival on the ward unsurprisingly brought him into contact with a wholesale change of staff from those who he'd seen before. The staff nurse was aware of Colin's involvement with the family, even though Stephanie was no longer a patient on ward twenty-four. She would be transferred to intensive care upon returning from theatre following brain surgery.

The staff nurse was, however, unable to share with Colin any other details since her ward had not featured in Stephanie's emergency admission. Dr Purcell was not there either. She would have been either on one of the other paediatric wards or in A&E. This placed Colin at something of a quandary, since he didn't know exactly what he might do, nor where he might go. He was effectively at a complete loss, in thought, word and deed.

As he made his way into that now familiar corridor to leave ward twenty-four, he was met by another member of staff with a visitor in tow. "Is it Mr Millwood?" the nurse hesitantly enquired.

"Ye-es," Colin answered dubiously.

"I'm D. C. Hibbett from Chatterton CID," the visitor boldly interjected. "Could I have a word?" Colin readily agreed, of course. This was a familiar name to him, though he did not believe that he had ever met this particular detective before. The nurse quickly showed them through to the ward office, before closing the door behind her as she left.

Adopting a distinctly formal tone, Mr Hibbett promptly asked, "Am I right in thinking you are the social worker for Stephanie Finch then, Mr Millwood?"

"Well, not exactly," Colin replied. "I'm actually a senior social worker. I supervise the family social worker, Ms Quayle."

"Okay then, Mr Millwood. You're probably aware that we have Wendy Finch in custody?" to which Colin nodded accordingly. "Right then," the detective continued, "we'll need to take possession of the social services file."

"Yes?" replied Colin inquisitively, though strongly suspecting which way this was heading.

"Well, we require your file. Please." The detective clumsily added the courtesy by way of an afterthought.

"I'm afraid I don't have it," Colin replied, feeling an element of rising indignation.

"Well, you'll need to get it then, from wherever it might be," D. C. Hibbett returned in an evidently uncompromising manner.

Colin urged himself to stay cool and to not say anything he might subsequently regret. "I am telling you that I don't have it, and, more to the point, even if I had, I would not necessarily have the authority to blithely hand it over to someone else on the basis of a simple request – polite or otherwise." Indignation then welled further, in spite of acknowledged wisdom to the contrary.

D. C. Hibbett then took half a pace towards him and said, looking him firmly in the eye, "Mr Millwood, I'm telling you that before this day is out, we shall be in possession of your file."

"Well, there you go then, Mr Hibbett," Colin almost trilled with a smile, "you evidently don't need any help from me. I'll bid you goodday." He thereby left him – albeit speechless – to get on with it. He would really have to share the events of the past twenty-four hours with his own senior staff.

When he got home, still in an exceedingly troubled state, Colin was eventually able to speak to his area officer, May Overton, who, in turn, would brief their higher chain of command. The local authority really would need to brace itself to anticipate a bombardment of questions from any number of different sources.

TWO

Having to think the unthinkable

COLIN EMERGED FROM ANOTHER troubled night half-inclined to pinch himself to escape the clutches of a hideous nightmare. It was no good. It was all real. Having washed and dressed in a semi-trance, he kissed Helen goodbye to head to work and face the music. He had already made up his mind to walk the three miles or so to the office just to think it all through. Walking to work was the most desirable option. After all, there would be little need for a car merely in fielding rounds of repercussions. Of course, there could be no guarantee that this would not in any case spell the end of his career.

As he ambled along, with no sense of urgency, he struggled to assimilate how the vivid brightness of a sunlit sky could possibly encompass such harsh realities on a troubled earth below. He kept turning over in his mind how he could possibly have so misread the world in which Stephanie had lived. Wendy arrested, and in custody!

His mind then flashed to thoughts of young Emmie Quayle. "Whatever will she think?" he said audibly to himself as he walked along. His valiant attempt at relieving her from weekend commitments had so cruelly backfired. He felt he had dreadfully let her down. Prospects loomed again of suspension, or worse. Self-condemnation just railed incessantly, from one dismal prospect to another.

Colin eventually reached the narrow street containing the Chatterton district social work office. Realising it had been open for half an hour or more, he rationalised his technically late arrival in terms of it representing only a fraction of the futile time he'd spent at the hospital over the weekend. Stopping momentarily at the entrance to gaze at the edifice above, he wondered if this could possibly be for the last time.

Taking a deep breath, he pushed open the outer door. "Oh Colin!" the young receptionist, Rita, gasped as he stepped into the admin office. "How are you, Colin?" As he forced a passive smile, the familiar Monday morning banter fell silent. Tears welled visibly in Rita's eyes and were proof enough that Colin's wretched tale of woe was already the centre of office news. Quickly snatching items of post from his pigeon-hole, he hurriedly made good his escape upstairs to his office.

"Oh, Colin!" May Overton exclaimed as he tried to dash unnoticed past her open door. Stepping inside, head bowed, he gently, and for some reason slowly and precisely, closed the door behind him.

As he tried to find an appropriate opening, Mrs Overton forestalled him. "Come and sit down, Colin," she said kindly. "I was not necessarily expecting to see you this morning. How are you feeling?"

That was an easy one, Colin thought. "I don't know, May," he gasped, head still bowed. "I don't know what to think… about anything. I simply cannot understand how we may have managed to get it so wrong. It's not been a case to which we have been even remotely indifferent. In spite of all that has happened since we first became involved, we have never really considered it to be about child abuse; not in real terms. We had been supporting a struggling single-parent through a housing transfer."

As he lifted his head towards his manager, he noticed the Finch family case file on the desk in front of her. He took another deep breath. "It's okay, Colin," she said, on realising he'd seen it. "Mike Colburn has asked me to secure it on behalf of the director. He has lined up someone in HQ to go through it all to draft him an overview of the case." Colin might have expected that at the very least. If there was anything to remotely feel confident about, Emmie's file would be largely up to date. Even better though, it would certainly place it beyond D. C. Ray Hibbett's reach.

"What do you want to do, Colin?" May asked, still kindly, sporting a characteristically broad smile. "You don't need to be here, you know. Wouldn't you prefer a day off? It could be taken in lieu of all the time you spent on the case over the weekend. It's whatever you wish to do, Colin." He took a degree of encouragement from this being a matter of his choice. It was not about his being asked to step back, or worse.

"Brooding over it at home is not the answer, May," he said. "There may be advantages in my having other things to focus on at work, or even in my being around to answer any emerging queries about the case."

"Okay," May said. "Fair enough, then. Though Alwyn Timms" – a senior social worker colleague of Colin's, who supervised one of Chatterton's long-term case-management teams – "is making arrangements for someone to keep in touch with Cheryl Finch at her maternal grandmother's." Colin winced at this. Amid waves of acute anxiety over Stephanie, he had not given Cheryl a second thought. He was more than happy to go along with May's suggestion.

When he eventually reached the Intake team room, he was met with an atmosphere of consuming solace from colleagues present. Emmie Quayle was first to rise immediately to her feet to take hold of Colin's upper arm in an affectionately supportive way. "Oh, Colin," was all she could say, though nothing more was remotely necessary. This spontaneous gesture of condolence from Emmie was particularly consoling. It meant more to him than she would ever know.

"Morning, folks," he murmured passively. "I'll bring you up to speed on matters arising as business unfolds. Meanwhile, Phill," he said, addressing Phill Vernon, one of the more experienced duty officers that morning, "has anything of note arisen so far today?"

"Not yet," Phill replied, "but don't worry, Colin. Leave it to Gill and me. We'll only bother you if it's really necessary." Colin nodded grateful thanks, before asking Emmie to spare him a few moments in his office.

As she was taking a seat, Colin said, with a sigh, "Well, Emmie, I certainly didn't make much success of covering for you did I?"

"I'm not sure that any of us would have been anticipating this," she replied. "Taking Stephanie to hospital on Friday was about our needing to be clear about the nature of her injuries rather than our having particular suspicions about them. It's what our procedures require us to do. What did the paediatricians make of them, Colin?"

"Dr Corke said they were not particularly suspicious, not in harmful areas. In letting him know of the nature of your involvement with the family in recent weeks, I explained how we had regarded the child's successive bumps and bruises largely in terms of rough-and-tumble. While that of course raised matters of parental supervision that you have been addressing, beyond that we were largely working towards the housing transfer." Emmie nodded in agreement.

"There must have been something else, though, beyond that," Colin mused with a furrowed brow. "Whatever happened on Saturday night could have been something else."

"Something that we missed?" posed Emmie nervously.

"I'm not sure," Colin replied thoughtfully. "It could have been. On the other hand, it could have been something that was purposely kept from us or that had otherwise happened quite out of the blue. It may become clearer in due course, but we may never get to know what it was. Time may tell. In the meantime," he continued, "how are *you* feeling right now?"

"I'm gobsmacked," she replied emphatically. "I just hope it doesn't undermine my ability to form a view about another case ever again."

"You and me both," agreed Colin. "Once we are aware of this week's demands by way of aftermath, we'll find an additional supervision slot by Friday at the latest." This was duly agreed. "I have to say though, Emmie," he added. "I feel much better for just having seen you and beginning to collect our thoughts in this way."

Thereafter, Colin was able to throw himself, to at least some extent, into wider Intake team business. Much of that inevitably concerned trying to meet the myriad of familiar needs besetting elderly people, particularly those living alone. This was not just about peoples' physical frailty though. Where physical limitations become complicated by the effects of social isolation, or even poverty – made more acute back then in the wake of the long-running coal strike – the impact upon elderly people, among others, could be endless.

Billy Lumsden entered the team room, having conducted a home visit on his way to work that morning. His glowing smile evidently indicated that he had not yet caught up with Finch family news. His mirth, however, had been the product of a visit he had just made to one Bertha Keeling. She was a lady in her nineties who was well-known to Chatterton's Intake social workers. Bertha was renowned for the obstinate way she clung to independence despite the onset of old age. She refused endless offers of help and support that would successively be made on her behalf by social services.

Billy had made this latest visit in the wake of concerns latterly expressed for Bertha by her neighbours. He and Bertha were well known to one another in enacting this familiar charade. Billy's broad smile persisted as he announced that on this latest trip to see Bertha, having spent time generally chatting together, Billy broached again the prospect of her perhaps having weekly help. On this occasion, however, it became apparent from the earnest look on her face that Bertha may have at last begun to give the matter some serious consideration.

This inclined Billy to seize upon the opportunity of gently pursuing it, by adding, "What about a spot of say, some home help then, Bertha, in assisting with weekly chores?"

At this, Bertha retreated promptly to her position of entrenched refusal by saying, "Oh no, Mr Lumsden. No, I won't have that. I'm past cleaning for folk at my age."

"She wasn't joking either," Billy told them. "She was perfectly serious!"

This fleeting sliver of glee, introduced so unwittingly by Billy, went some way in lifting an air of collective gloom. A typically busy Monday morning then moved things on considerably towards business as usual. While the eventual end of the working day had not completely shaken Colin free from agonies of the Finches, he suddenly realised that he had no means of transport home. Myra Jackson, however, one of Intake's social work assistants who lived not far from Colin, saved him from having to walk all the way home again.

Myra used this opportunity to bring her senior up to date with a visit that she too had made that morning to a relatively isolated old lady. She was again someone who others often felt would benefit from help at home. This particular lady, however, persistently refused to answer her door to any callers whom she did not recognise. While this inclination, of course, had its own merits for someone in her position, Myra Jackson was among those whose genuine calls inevitably proved futile. The elderly lady's abiding reticence caused her evident need for support to fall disproportionately upon her only daughter, who worked full-time and who lived some distance away.

On this particular morning, however, Myra had pre-arranged to meet the daughter at her mother's home as a means of at last making productive initial contact. Myra was well received and the lady's daughter explained some of the difficulties arising from her mother's general forgetfulness. It favourably turned out, however, that she was not inclined to refuse genuine offers of help and assistance put to her in that way. They therefore proceeded to identify some simple options.

Upon prospects of help being mutually agreed, the daughter then announced loudly, taking account of her mother's poor hearing, "Now look here, Mother, you've got to let this lady in. She's from the government!" Myra was suitably impressed by this elevation of importance, so she wondered if it might bring any matching elevation in salary. Colin smiled while regrettably having to disappoint her. This episode brought another fleeting escape from the despondency absorbing him. It even caused him to wonder whether it could have even been the product of orchestrated support from loyal colleagues.

These spasmodic glimmers, however, were unlikely to forge any lasting relief from the troubles gripping him. Before the week was out, that scale of trauma escalated upon news of little Stephanie's life-support being discontinued. This also meant that Wendy Finch was consequently charged with murder.

It considerably raised the profile of the Finch family overview that was in the midst of preparation in social services HQ. Its author was one Patrick Yates, HQ's senior research officer, who was widely considered to adopt a "holier than thou" attitude in his expressed application and analysis of social work practice. He was also thought to consider himself a confidant of the director, without this necessarily being a perception shared by the wider workforce, including senior managers.

Patrick's overview of the management of the case in question turned out, for many staff interested in understanding the truth of it all, to be a surprisingly underwhelming disappointment. It did not reveal anything that was otherwise unknown to those variously involved with the family, save one exception. Its major finding – emphasised in Patrick's eloquent tones of wisdom – was that a case conference should have taken place given those successive visits to hospital. This formal meeting of professionals directly involved with a child or family was convened upon the potential for risks to a child or children becoming apparent in view of their care or treatment. The conference formed the basis for collaboratively agreeing ways forward in managing or reducing identified risks on an inter-agency basis. It had become a common feature of professional practice in taking action to protect children that had evolved over the preceding decade.

"There should've been a case conference," Mike Colburn repeated from time to time, when he came to meet the Chatterton staff who had been involved in the case. May Overton was present, together with Colin, Emmie and Gill Norwood, since it was Gill who had made initial contact with the family. This appeared to represent the extent of social services' official response in reviewing what had taken place and in advising of any further action following the death of a child.

"But we were in touch with all of the agencies involved," Colin protested mildly. "Apart from ourselves, there was only the nursery, the health visitor and the doctors who examined Stephanie when she was seen in hospital. No one – none of us – was able to explain those injuries beyond the effects of rough-and-tumble."

"There should still have been a conference though," Colburn insisted yet again, "to actively eliminate any other issues or suspicions on an inter-agency basis. We have a parent here, Colin, who has just been charged with murder no less." Colin duly acceded to the harsh reality of that. He didn't need reminding. While having a conference might have indeed been the least that should have happened, with head bowed, he privately doubted the difference it would have made in revealing all about family Finch. That only served to reignite his own embarrassing recollections about his discussion with Dr Corke. He was still shamefully unaware of any details of father figures for either child.

The murder charge unsurprisingly moved the police investigation up a gear. Detectives wanted to speak to Emmie Quayle, though that request came formally from the Detective Inspector, via May Overton. It was not left to D. C. Ray Hibbett's subtle way with words. Alwyn Timms accompanied Emmie for that interview, largely as a passive observer to support the young social worker. That albeit minor role for Alwyn helpfully corresponded with his perspective of supervising the social worker engaged in monitoring Cheryl's welfare at her grandmother's. Emmie and Alwyn each independently reported afterwards how they had found the interview straightforward. It was largely information gathering, apart from Emmie being asked directly if she had ever witnessed Wendy being abusive towards her children. Emmie said that she hadn't. No mention was otherwise made of the police being at all interested in accessing the case file.

News of Emmie being interviewed by police reverberated around Chatterton district office like wildfire. Mary Ewart, another experienced member of the Intake team, confided to Colin how she had overheard two workers from another team discussing the case in the office kitchen. One of them felt that social workers like Emmie, who are not themselves parents, cannot possibly be expected to really appreciate the 'ins and outs' of parenting.

"Whatever did you make of that, Mary?" Colin asked in surprise.

"I put her straight, I can tell you," Mary replied confidently. "I told her that it was a parent who appears to have been held responsible for the travesties of the case they were discussing. Getting our heads round family life, I stressed, is as much about having once been a child, like any other member of a family, as anything else. I didn't await any further discussion though. I'd have been there all morning."

Thereafter, much of the global angst surrounding the Finches gradually began to subside amid the familiar range of routine work-related distractions for Chatterton social workers. Elsewhere, however, there were endless work-a-day reminders for Colin, even in sport and entertainment no less, that served only to reignite his residual misgivings about Stephanie's tragic death. He was often struck by ways in which the context of his own sorrow could somehow be projected onto news headlines that seize so compellingly upon the advent of tragedy.

Within a matter of weeks, there had been successive disasters at football grounds – so often the pinnacles of joy and achievement – with more than fifty people losing their lives in a ferocious fire at Valley Parade in Bradford and over thirty deaths following the collapse of a wall during the European Cup Final at the Heysel stadium in Brussels. Those horrors, however, were later to be eclipsed, to some extent, when more than ninety spectators were to lose their lives at Hillsborough four years later. Beyond that, relatively few weeks continued to elapse between world-wide airline disasters.

If the sequel to Emmie's police interview had subsequently brought any welcome respite locally from negative repercussions of the Finch family tragedy, it was short-lived. The calm before the storm was breached by evening newspaper headlines announcing the beginning of the mother's Crown Court trial for murdering her child. Evening updates during the week incorporated a wave of angry comments from individuals within the local community, who were highly critical of what social workers must have missed on little Stephanie's behalf.

A number of people were swift to claim how often they had seen members of the wider family striking the child. Others had apparently witnessed an aunt compelling Cheryl to sit on the floor with her legs straight out in front of her and to press down the palms of her hands on the floor by her sides. She had to remain there in silence for a considerable time by way of punishment for minor misdemeanours. Perhaps equally difficult to understand, was why none of those episodes was subsequently reported to a responsible authority at the time, even to the police.

Almost as alarming for Colin, the paediatric registrar who had seen Stephanie during her hospital admission culminating in the child's fateful discharge home, apparently told the court of his warning the child's mother about the effects of excessive chastisement. Colin found this exasperating. None of that was mentioned to him, by anyone.

Other evidence extended to statements of Cheryl being the product of a sexual assault on Wendy by an unnamed male. Clearly it had taken the scrutiny of a Crown Court to divulge these more searching elements of family history. They certainly went far beyond what people had ever been willing to share earlier with social workers. "It just goes to show," Colin lamented in a meeting with May and Emmie to keep abreast of trial progress, "how all of this has been like trying to see round corners."

The outcome of the trial saw Wendy Finch imprisoned for manslaughter. It was stated how, on that fateful evening, as Wendy was getting ready to go out with her new boyfriend, Stephanie had protested volubly at being left with a babysitter, who could have been her aunt. Wendy apparently hit out randomly towards her daughter. This caused her to fall, banging her head against a wooden doorframe.

There was no satisfaction for Colin in any of that. It brought no closure for him. This was in spite of the staff involved in the case being defended robustly by the Chairman of the Social Services Committee in later editions of evening newspapers. For Colin, by another eerie twist of fate, national headlines were later that week filled with news of yet another airline disaster. The crash of a domestic flight in Japan had claimed the lives of more than five hundred people and was said to be the worst air disaster in aviation history.

Surely though, he kept thinking to himself, *it can't be about life and death every time.* In enduring this dreadful aftermath, he would clutch desperately at vivid recollections of those more rewarding episodes of his twelve years of social work practice. Even as a 'green' novice, way back, his genuine commitment in just wanting to help people – or rather to encourage them to help themselves – had been the essence of his social work vision. Children suffering harrowing deaths surely lived elsewhere, in far-flung inner cities, not around more amiable avenues of Chatterton.

Occasional broken nights' sleep would reawaken Colin's shimmering memories of seemingly halcyon days; of happier times, not so long ago. While family life had reputations of its own for seldom being trouble-free, his distant recollections were not consumed by such acute despair… or were they?

THREE

Competing past priorities

COLIN'S UNRAVELLING RECOLLECTIONS FROM times past, during the earlier stages of his career, pitched him into well-rehearsed conundrums about the best interests of children. In these circumstances, his thoughts would inevitably be consumed by searing dilemmas surrounding his first really challenging child welfare case several years previously. For some reason, such quandaries had a familiar habit of presenting themselves on Fridays. Presumably this was since Friday effectively brought two days grace to the making or breaking of critical decisions.

Getting those decisions wrong, he appreciated, way back then, including unforgivably missed opportunities by social workers, had so easily become the stuff of legend. The outpouring of public rage held no bounds. Errors of professional judgement about what should have plainly happened are collectively analysed by the wider media, among others, in occupying much higher planes of wisdom. How haplessly it seemed that genuinely committed, professional 'do-gooders' could be so flagrantly scorned by any number of cynics.

All of this consumed Colin's morbid Friday feelings as he continually turned over in his mind the circumstances of that first child welfare case that he had worked with in the Longley locality at that time. It was a family that had caused him real concern. His newly-qualified status had brought him increasingly familiar with ways in which high-profile cases concerning child ill-treatment become infinitely better appreciated through the faultless medium of hindsight.

The family occupying Colin's thoughts were in many ways not untypical of many who lurch from one crisis to another. For them, the paradox of family life is that it can be, on one hand, so effortlessly uncomplicated, yet, in other respects, it is seldom that simple. It also follows that, for anyone charged with the challenge of trying to help, or indeed, to offer any semblance of support – or even charity – finely balanced judgements need to be made. The line between what is just about acceptable, and that which is not, can be paper-thin. This was at the core of Colin's inescapable unease.

Expectations of public confidence in social workers in the field of child welfare had been written large a decade earlier by the circumstances of a little girl in Brighton. That child, seven-year-old Maria, had so graphically caught public imagination when she was reportedly wheeled to hospital in a pram by her stepfather, who would later serve time for her manslaughter. The subsequent public inquiry into the brutality of Maria's death had tragically revealed an unrelenting, dismal family life. Denied many commonplace treats or favours, even of merely being bought an ice cream, she was consigned to looking on longingly, as such simple gestures were otherwise bestowed generously upon favoured brothers and sisters.

The public scrutiny that followed, however, had simultaneously revealed infamous failings by professionals that were to herald a new dawn of professional practice in this area of work. It importantly introduced the notion of 'non-accidental injury' to children into professional vocabulary for the next decade. For Colin's part though, if he were blatantly honest, he was ashamed to have not actually read any full accounts of that inquiry's findings beyond the sordid headlines.

He hardly dared envisage the prospect of similar misfortune now befalling the Finch family currently occupying his thoughts. The wider public could be forgiven for wondering what on earth social services had been playing at. Feeling compelled to think it all through again, surely there could not be any parallels here with Maria's forlorn circumstances. Or could there?

"What's to be done?" he had asked himself years before, upon agonizing over his first child welfare case. This had him swinging his old Triumph Toledo into a quiet side street, just to think.

All the social workers on Colin's team were well acquainted with this familiar neighbourhood within the wider area covered by the Longley area office. Remaining deep in thought, Colin slowly and purposefully applied his handbrake, pulling up alongside the wire fence of the local primary school.

He wondered if this fragile set of family circumstances would survive another weekend. What has to happen before social workers finally get around to taking decisive action on behalf of young children living in such an undesirable environment? These doubts extended to his capacity – as a relatively inexperienced social worker, moreover the product of a comparatively privileged grammar school upbringing – in bringing about meaningful change to benefit the Grattage family, of all people.

On the other hand, he pondered, what actual evidence exists of serious neglect here? Moreover, were its effects upon the individual children enough to irrefutably persuade a court? Colin reflected again upon the nature of his visit to the family that day, and indeed upon more than one visit he had made that week.

The Grattage family was widely known on the Sparrow Park Estate, both to professionals and, not least, to their neighbours. Tommy and June Grattage had four children whose ages ranged from ten months to ten years. The oldest, Dawn, was a convivial child, relatively happily disposed, who seemed to derive satisfaction from assuming a degree of adult responsibility in sharing the care of her younger siblings.

For her part, however, June was not a good role model. She was not very bright. She was disorganised, generating few initiatives in establishing household routines. To what extent, however, June had herself benefited from any positive role model was far from clear. Although she came from a local family, there did not appear to be any real evidence of wider family support, nor indeed, of any extended family interaction in terms of even occasional family gatherings.

Tommy, meanwhile, was predictably of little assistance. He appeared to regard active parenting as women's work. He was effectively unemployed, beyond the scope of occasional cash-in-hand casual labour – apart from burglary indeed. He had a considerable criminal record, largely for petty theft in harbouring a particular proclivity for stealing bicycles. Sadly though, Tommy did not have a reputation for being in any way a gifted thief. He and his premises were often the first among routine enquiries that police would make in investigating local crime. Officers would often be rewarded by quickly recovering the stolen goods in question in or around Tommy's property.

Michael was the second child, aged eight. He was a man's man, very much into rough-and-tumble, though there was little or no evidence of Tommy's engagement with or even interest in the lad. Michael's boundless energy cried out to be channelled in constructive, outward ways, but any hope of that from within the family was plainly too much to expect.

Then came the two youngest children, Susan, aged five, and ten-month-old Terry. Susan was extremely placid, craving little more than the comforts and company of her elder sister. While that met with considerable reciprocation, Terry meanwhile appeared to make little impression on family life at all. He was seldom seen out of his pushchair.

In every respect, the children and the premises in which the family lived were frankly dirty, if not conforming to the familiar idiom of being 'filthy dirty'. Efforts apparently made by a succession of previous social workers and health visitors to motivate Tommy and June to raise domestic standards had proved futile, bearing in mind that any professional contact would have largely been with June.

Voluminous social work case records, consisting of a series of handwritten entries by different workers, at different times – in different coloured ballpoint ink – spoke largely for themselves when the dog-eared cover of the case file was opened. Within the records, and indeed during extensive visits by that succession of workers, Tommy would be absent on any number of different pretexts.

It was this unpunctuated lack of progress in virtually any aspect of family life, and the impact of all of that upon the children's prospects, that returned to trouble Colin again. How bad did it need to get before something simply had to be done? If so, what form would 'something' look like? Has the point of no return yet been unequivocally reached in resorting to non-negotiable, statutory intervention? On the other hand, despite all of these shortcomings, there were glimmering indications that June really loved her kids. They were not, after all, at risk of the sorts of life-threatening misfortune that had so infamously befallen little Maria, in Brighton, all those years ago. Or were they?

Colin eventually found himself reconciled to the premise that dirty hands and dirty faces were not life threatening. The essence of child welfare was surely not about life and death in every case. Social work was, after all, about helping people, wasn't it? It was really about helping people to find their own solutions to their difficulties. This was indeed a society where settling for 'good enough' parenting would later become a widely regarded, well-informed idiom of professional practice.

Then again, a somewhat naïve professional appreciation of the effects of child neglect may not have then been untypical of a widespread 'gung-ho' approach to social work. This relatively new profession was much driven by enthusiasm, sometimes at the expense of the wisdom of applied science. Colin, for his part, wondered whether any effective means of shielding children from abuse was more of an art than of any form of science. He was, however, certainly in no mood to give up.

With renewed determination, he resolved to reflect further upon his whole past week of 'Grattaging' with Cora, his senior social worker, back at the office. But, as he leaned forward to turn his key in the ignition, Colin became aware of someone watching him. A smiling face, vividly illuminated by bright teeth, was peering through the wire fence of the adjacent school playground.

This was a face he knew well. It was that of ten-year-old Donna, with whose family he had been in contact some weeks previously. That particularly memorable episode had culminated in Colin driving away at speed from the family home with Donna, together with her mum, Tracey, and Donna's younger sister, Myra, to ferry mother and daughters to a women's refuge some distance away. The circumstances of that hasty departure effectively constituted their dramatic escape from the fearful grasp of the children's father, D'wain.

Tracey was still sporting yellowing facial bruising that represented telling reminders of the downturn in her relationship with D'wain in recent months. His all-too-familiar resort to verbal, and then physical aggression had latterly driven his loyal wife to breaking point. It had incrementally reached the ultimate resort of Tracey needing to break free from the oppressive clutches of a man who she had once adored.

For Colin, however, Donna's glowing smile through the fence brought modestly redeeming measures of reassurance. While he could never completely reconcile himself to the merits of effecting a family's such dramatic departure from home, this happy face might just be indicating that the children were beginning to acquire some means of equilibrium, at least in restoring familiar links with school and local friends.

To what extent it may have represented any sort of stability returning to their lives, obviously remained to be seen. Colin had unfortunately not been able to begin to find any opportunity – from a combination of his own complacency and a raft of other priorities – for exploring with Donna and Myra their feelings about their dad and how they might wish to remain in touch with him.

There had never been any suggestion of D'wain being anything other than a good father to his daughters. Colin needed to find time to establish the extent to which they might have been coming to terms with any negative reactions from the separation and loss of their dad. If only he had had nothing else to do!

FOUR

Cradles to graves

DRIVING BACK TO THE office in Fording Street with very mixed thoughts surrounding two very different families, Colin decided to take a minor detour. He would make what he tended to regard as an 'easy' visit to end the week. This was to Doris Betts, an elderly lady for whom he had considerable admiration.

Doris, one of Colin's distinctly varied caseload, was in receipt of local authority services as an elderly person with certain physical disabilities. Her mobility was restricted to the degree that she required disability aids to help maintain her independence. She was also considered, within the formal scope of statutory welfare provision, to be socially isolated as a result of this restricted mobility.

Supportive services to elderly people, together with disabled adults, represented only one of three broad aspects of welfare reform that had been generated by the creation of social services departments in the early 1970s.

That new welfare agenda effectively unified three broadly defined local authority services that had hitherto been provided by three distinctly separate council departments.

The Children's Department had previously provided a range of services to children and young people, like Donna and Myra and those in the Grattage family. The Mental Health Department had provided support and services to adults affected broadly by mental health and learning difficulties. Then, thirdly, The Welfare Department provided services to elderly people, to adults who were 'registered' as chronically sick and disabled and also, interestingly, to homeless families.

The rationale for this welfare-driven reform lay largely in the uncomplicated wisdom of trying to avoid the duplication of professional intervention for families. Those visited by people from different local authority departments, albeit with an apparently different focus – but with considerable elements of overlap in commonly addressing the potential for 'social breakdown' – could be overwhelming. This was particularly apparent to those finding themselves faced with a veritable affliction of do-gooders.

This unusual prospect, of having to contend with more than one council representative, was only true for those families facing more than one of those particular aspects of social need. Now in these emancipated times, modern thinking craved having only one person with whom any combination of these difficulties could be discussed. This had thereby become the era of 'generic' social work, where one worker's sole input into family life was effortlessly intended to eradicate any ham-fisted duplication of effort in getting to grips with family circumstances. It proved to be, however, one of those ideas that might have been fine in theory, persisting reliably for twenty years or so, before its unsurprising limitations were eventually laid bare.

Colin was indeed one of this new breed of generic social workers, finding himself attracted to this modern ideology before becoming enticed into a social work career from the relatively predictable world of teaching. This first social work post following his professional qualification had pitched Colin into the local area office in Longley, where he sought to provide help and services across that wide spectrum of social need to individuals of all ages.

He was a member of the Intake team there. This consisted of a team of social workers providing initial advice and assistance to people reported – or who would otherwise present themselves – to their local social services department as being 'in need' of social work services.

The Intake label was simply another contemporary term for what was otherwise known as a 'duty team', operating a responsive service to people within their 'patch-based' locality. Longley was one of five such social services area offices in this Midlands metropolitan authority, serving a population of nearly two hundred thousand people.

Where family problems proved to be more complex, including those clearly associated with longer-term health or relationship difficulties, this could elevate social work input to specific elements of mandatory legal intervention. Intake social workers would usually provide help and support in making an initial assessment of the necessary action to be undertaken. Responsibility for carrying out further work would then transfer to another worker on a long-term team, located within the same area office, to deliver the necessary supportive input over time.

In this context, Colin might have justifiably transferred responsibility for supporting Doris Betts to one of his longer-term colleagues some months previously. It concerned him, though, that Doris did not necessarily have altogether pressing needs once she had been provided with disability aids. She did not really warrant any ongoing priority among long-term caseloads heaving with increasing numbers of elderly people. So she remained among a handful of cases that Colin kept 'open', by either maintaining intermittent contact or by simply retaining files largely on a 'dormant' basis.

By retaining people's files in this way, without any current action necessarily being taken, social workers were able to respond with familiar knowledge upon that individual needing to contact social services again. This avoided their having to explain their circumstances all over again and brought additional benefits of continuity and of conveying to people that they were more than just a number in a static filing system.

While Doris Betts might not have had really pressing needs, she was nonetheless a housebound elderly widow living alone. She had no close family beyond a niece in Clacton and a nephew in King's Lynn. She received fortnightly home help through social services, to help with certain household chores and shopping.

A young woman named Natalie, who had recently moved in next-door with her husband and two young children, had latterly begun to call in occasionally offering to run other errands. Colin had seen Natalie in passing at Doris's on a couple of occasions. Her bleached blonde hair rendered her virtually unmistakable, particularly in its tufted style. Colin thought that people could be forgiven for thinking that Natalie might have actually been electrocuted.

Doris had intermittently rejected further offers of help aimed at offsetting the effects of her relative isolation. In those respects, she may have been resolutely different from many other people. She was not a moaner, nor was she interested in charity. She was rather one of the 'old-school', the product of a generation that had once vowed never to surrender, and this stoic attitude was a mantle she wore with pride.

Colin regarded her as inspirational in these respects, even to the point of his regarding visits to Doris as something of a tonic. She was someone on whom he could legitimately call in the course of his duties in otherwise seeking some sort of asylum from a world consumed by the vagaries of social despair. This past week had certainly been one from which less taxing work would bring a welcome diversion. Moreover, Doris also made exceptionally good milky coffee, complemented no less by chocolate biscuits.

Doris answered her door, leaning heavily and characteristically on her two sticks. She beamed on seeing Colin, welcoming him warmly, with the accompanying background strains of Frank Ifield's 'She taught me to yodel' resonating merrily indoors. "Hello, Doris. Just called to see how you are doing," he said cheerily, and trying to compete with the yodelling.

"All the better for seeing you," Doris almost sang in reply, before she turned to lead a well-trodden, single-file procession to her favourite easy chair in the living room. Here, Doris thankfully leaned forward to bring Frank Ifield to an abrupt close.

"Anything need doing while I'm here?" Colin asked.

"Just sit yourself down," she said, still beaming. "I've got some official-looking forms for you to look at for me but they will do for another time." Doris's polite declining of offers of help was by no means unusual. "I can't be bothered with them now. They'll have to wait."

This freed Colin to spend a pleasant half hour or so chatting to Doris. His only exertion was that of politely declining a second cup of sweet milky coffee before, and without a word, he casually set about washing up the handful of dishes to conclude their mutually rewarding half-hour. He really did need to get back to the office.

Turning into the car park at the rear of his office, he was met with a timely reminder that it was Friday afternoon. The car park was more than half empty, in sharp contrast to virtually any other working day when spaces would be at a premium.

Colin was greeted with customary cheerfulness, and a chorus of "Hiya"s, on entering the office by two of the admin assistants, Pam and Karen. "Any messages?" he asked.

"Don't think so," said Karen, still cheerily, but without looking up from her filing index. Then she added, while still concentrating on the task before her, "Oh, can you ring Jim Rathbone back? It can't be urgent though 'cos he's not in now till Monday."

As Colin uttered modest thanks, Pam called out that there were only a handful of horses left in the office sweepstake. "For tomorrow's National. It's fifty pence a go," she said, eagerly pushing a box of tickets towards him.

"Go on then," Colin said complacently, nowhere nearly matching Pam's fizzing enthusiasm. "I'll have a couple." He shoved his hand into the box containing the remaining tickets before nonchalantly handing two tickets back to Pam, who, still giggling with eagerness, was itching to find out what he he'd drawn.

"Hmm," said Pam, unfolding the first ticket. "So and So," she announced. "Don't know if that's any good," she pondered, before unfolding the second ticket. "Oh, Jimmy Miff," she said with another burst of enthusiasm, and she handed both tickets back to Colin. He shrugged with a good-natured smile. The Grand National really meant little to him, let alone either of his selections.

"I've got Royal Stuart. Karen's drawn the bookies' favourite, Rubstic," Pam continued triumphantly. She was still bubbling with excitement as she put the box away in concluding this evident entertainment. There did not appear to be many other people around other offices, largely conforming to the state of the Friday afternoon car park.

"Is Cora in?" Colin asked. He was eager to consult with his senior social work supervisor upon his mixed emotions surrounding the Grattage family, and not least to seek some sort of endorsement to a continuingly precarious policy of 'wait and see' in endeavouring to support them.

"She's down at the hut," replied Karen, "in a meeting with some of the IT staff."

"Never mind," said Colin, "I suppose it can wait now till next week."

The hut was a pre-fabricated building further down Fording Street, towards the town centre. It had been utilised as an office building in the pre-social services era and it had more recently accommodated the current area social work teams before they moved into their modern, purpose-built premises. The new area office was readily identifiable in conforming to an authority-wide design, coinciding with the heralding of this revolutionary new dawn of social services departments.

Interestingly though, Karen's reference to IT staff back then had nothing to do with computer software. This was, after all, in an era where a great deal of administrative methodology characteristically relied heavily upon blue biros. It harked back of course to those days before people had ever taken to wearing their glasses idly on the tops of their heads.

IT in this particular context concerned Intermediate Treatment, another relatively more recent initiative within the field of juvenile offending, or juvenile justice as it later became known. Young people who had been brought before the juvenile court could be referred to Intermediate Treatment programmes. This was a resort, necessarily determined by the court, that was one of a range of options open to magistrates within a recognised 'tariff' of offending. It extended, particularly in respect of repeat offenders, to young people being committed into the care of the local authority in endeavouring to divert them from habitual offending behaviour.

IT thereby largely comprised a range of group activities in occupying this intended diversion from criminality and simultaneously aiming to generate young people's enthusiasm for other more legitimate interests. It could also include more direct, one-to-one contact with IT supervisors in addressing particular family-centred concerns in endeavouring to keep them out of trouble.

Since IT largely operated outside what might have been considered normal office hours, Cora Malone evidently valued the merits of making time to meet with IT staff in keeping pace with their work. She also took this opportunity to help in addressing any additional difficulties arising among some of the families with whom they were working.

Colin warmed to the thought of his supervisor making time to give priority to that sort of professional liaison. It reassured him that the Intake team at Longley was in such capable hands.

FIVE

Duty calls

IT WAS GOING TO be a relatively short weekend for Colin. It was his turn to be on the out-of-hours duty rota, through the night from 5pm on Saturday until 9am on Sunday. He would be one of three social workers 'on call' at home during that time, thereby making himself available to respond to emergency situations as and when required. A senior social worker would be first to field any such calls from members of the public and other organisations, who would be transferred from the council's operational services switchboard.

The senior social worker – similarly 'on call' at home – would determine whether emergency intervention by a social worker was necessary in any given set of circumstances. This meant that social workers on out-of-hours duty at home had to remain within earshot of their telephone during their shift. There were no mobile phones in those days.

While being 'on call' through the night was by no means guaranteed to consign staff to all-night commitments, weekends and bank holidays really did seem to comply with their own notorious reputations for testing the coping capacity of the wider public. Weekends, along with early evenings, are widely associated by social workers with being among those times when any simmering accumulation of family stress becomes wired to a distinctly shortened fuse.

On the other hand, Colin thought, should the Grattages happen to be referred to social services over this weekend, he could be readily on hand to respond with the benefit of his timely knowledge of family circumstances. Then again, he could find himself being challenged by what others might regard as casework shortfalls on the family's behalf, resulting in an 'out-of-hours' emergency. Shortly after 6.30pm, Colin had hardly got down to taking advantage of being on duty to put pen to paper with case recording, when the telephone rang. It was the familiar voice of the duty senior, Malcolm Miller, who Colin had got to know fairly well, even though they worked at different office locations.

"A thirteen-year-old," Malcolm explained, "by the name of Gemma Graham, from Marsden Mews in Wrinley, has been arrested for shoplifting in Wolverhampton. It seems she was one of a group of four friends who each attend the same high school and who will all be reported for summons on theft charges. Her mother, Mrs Graham, along with the other girls' parents, has attended the police station for her daughter's interview, but she is now refusing to have

Gemma back home. This shoplifting episode has been what she regards as the last straw. Wants Gemma in care."

Colin grimaced at the prospects of having to travel over to Wolverhampton, not to mention the familiar thought of drawn out rounds of argument in seeking any satisfactory way forward. He also had serious doubts, in any case, about the merits of local authority care being regarded as the only option in these circumstances.

"Is the family known to us?" Colin asked.

"Looks like Gemma had a previous caution for theft. Not much else, though there appears to have been a brief period of social work involvement last year. Nothing of note is appearing on the filing system though," Malcolm said in summary.

"Okay," said Colin. "I'll be there in about fifty minutes, depending on the scale of football traffic."

"Ask for Sergeant Twiss," Malcolm added. "He's your contact point."

Colin arrived at Wolverhampton police station well within the hour. As it happened, he had seen no football traffic. On arrival, he was shown to the custody suite where he fleetingly met Sergeant Twiss, the custody sergeant, who was standing behind a high desk and apparently poring over paperwork. He acknowledged Colin somewhat impassively, causing Colin to suspect that this middle-aged police officer, probably with umpteen years' service, might not spontaneously warm to social workers in any given circumstance.

"They are in there," announced Sergeant Twiss, nodding towards a nearby interview room. A young police officer showed Colin through to a not unfamiliar, featureless interview setting with frosted opaque windows. Mother and daughter were sitting together silently and motionless. Colin introduced himself, shaking hands with each of them in turn. He explained that he had only just arrived and that he would need to confirm the current progress of police enquiries before having a word with them.

Colin was intent upon extracting more than a dismissive nod from Sergeant Twiss and made the point that this might not simply be just another social work matter. The police officer thereupon became fractionally more forthcoming in explaining that four thirteen-year-olds from Wrinley had been seen stealing cosmetics from Boots by a store detective. While one of the girls had been found in possession of the goods in question, all four had been together in a group. Consequently, all four were to be reported for summons.

"Gemma has denied being involved in the theft," the sergeant said, "though she has a previous caution for theft, but her mother is not at all impressed by her daughter's involvement in this episode anyway, to the point that she is refusing to have her home. She has had to be persuaded to not abandon her daughter altogether here at the police station and to wait to speak to the social worker. There have apparently been other problems and she says this is the last straw. She wants Gemma in care."

Colin returned to the interview room to find mother and daughter still sitting silently side-by-side. Mrs Graham reiterated much of what had already been reported by the police.

"We can't do anything with her," she said. "She's all for her friends. You can see they're a bad influence. She does nothing at home, just wants to be out with them all the time."

"What do you make of all that?" asked Colin, trying hard to turn the question towards Gemma in a non-accusing way. Gemma said nothing. She merely shrugged her shoulders and fixed her gaze towards the floor.

"What about school?" Colin inquired. "How's that going for you?"

"'s all right," mumbled Gemma, with another shrug, and Colin took a shred of encouragement at even eliciting this minimal reply. He wondered though to what extent this young person's reticence was influenced by her immediate proximity to her mother.

"She's always done okay at school," Mrs Graham interjected. "There's never been any problem with attendance. She likes sport, but then again, that's where her friends are."

"School have never had occasion to report any problems? Colin asked.

"Not as far as I'm aware," replied Mrs Graham.

"Have you ever considered seeking assistance from social services before?" Colin asked, trying another approach.

"I went to social services last year," she replied. "Gemma had not been getting on with her dad. There were rows all the time, with me as well. He's not her real dad you see. Me and Gemma's real dad split up before she was born. Thank God," she emphasised by way of afterthought.

"What prompted you to go to social services?" asked Colin.

"I mentioned it to the doctor when I went to see him about something else. Dr Hamilton said I should go to social services and he gave me a letter to give to them."

"What became of that?" asked Colin.

"A really nice lady came round named Sally. I can't remember her second name. She spent time with Gemma, took her out a couple of times and also met with us as a family. I have a son as well you see, Michael. He's nine. Things seemed to go a bit better after that and Sally said we could get in touch again if ever we needed any further help."

"Is getting back to Sally your next step then?" suggested Colin.

"No way," said Mrs Graham angrily. "Not now. Not after this. She's pinched before. We've had enough. This takes the biscuit. How would you like it? See what you can do with her. We're finished." Her voice rose almost in crescendo, with gravitating expressions of anger, verging almost on hysteria.

"Okay," said Colin calmly. "Don't get upset."

"Upset!" she yelled. "I'll give you upset. Just take her with you! That's what you're here for isn't it? It serves her right; might just teach her a lesson."

"Okay, okay," said Colin again, trying hard now to appeal hopefully to her better nature in defusing this escalating emotion. "Let me get you fixed up with another cup of tea while I speak to Gemma on her own. I have to tell you though," he said, now adopting a more authoritative tone, "that my taking her away from here, wherever you think that might be, is not a simple option. It doesn't work like that. You perhaps need to appreciate that among a host of reasons for children coming into care, their needing to be taught lessons is certainly not among them."

Colin again sought the assistance of the young police officer, who appeared distinctly more amiable than his sergeant, in briefly separating mother and daughter. He returned quickly to Gemma, whose gaze remained solemnly fixed to the floor.

Any hopes and expectations, however, that he might have had about this dejected young person becoming more forthcoming in her mother's absence very quickly evaporated. 'All right' and 'okay' remained stock answers to virtually each and every sensitively posed question from Colin about family relationships and Gemma's views of school. Each dip into what might worry her, any hopes and ambitions she had and what she enjoyed most in life were all met by similarly indifferent shrugging of shoulders.

"Look," said Colin, almost in exasperation, "if I am going to be of any help to you, you will have to try and at least share with me your thoughts on the difficulties your mum describes." She remained similarly unmoved, beyond more shrugging upon Colin posing the ultimate query of her thoughts on the prospects of being received into local authority care. He actually wondered to what extent the threat of 'care' could be a stick Gemma might wish to wield to get back at her family for what she may have somehow regarded as her mother's betrayal.

At this next long pause, Colin began to despair at his fast disappearing range of options. He perceived

Gemma's unwavering resistance as a likely combination of stubbornness and of self-preservation in an unfamiliar situation. Beyond that, of course, he could not discount the possibility of this young person being depressed. He also fleetingly acknowledged the likely implications of a range of mixed emotions associated with the onset of adolescence, complicated by evident family tensions and step-parent relationships – but little of that was likely to be of relevance in this immediate crisis.

Colin invited Mrs Graham back into the room. She seemed now to be at least somewhat more composed. He explained how Gemma had not been inclined to give anything away, and how this could perhaps be attributed to her feeling an element of shame at the situation in which she now found herself, not for the first time.

On the other hand, as he felt obliged to point out to each of them, neither was Gemma expressing any concerns about life as she saw it. He asked Mrs Graham again whether she could find any merits in taking her daughter home and of working through these difficulties again, perhaps with further help from Sally.

"No, I'm not," said Mrs Graham, almost as firmly as before. "She'll have to go into care. I've had enough."

Then Colin engineered yet another pregnant pause before asking, in something of a hushed tone, "Mrs Graham, do you still love your daughter?"

She burst immediately into tears and, reaching out to Gemma, Mrs Graham spluttered through unfettered emotion, "Oh yes I do. Of course I do."

Gemma responded similarly and spontaneously in

what Colin saw as an unanticipated outpouring of mutual affection. The two became locked firmly in an extended, tearful embrace.

"I'll leave the two of you together for a couple of minutes," Colin said quietly, as he went outside to look for Sergeant Twiss.

"This could be game over," Colin said to the officer, trying hard not to punch the air with glee and almost whooping at this fortuitous success. "I think Mrs Graham will be taking Gemma home shortly. The local area office will be following up with the family next week on a number of issues surrounding today's events."

The police sergeant raised his eyebrows, grimacing an almost applauding nod towards the social worker. That was, however, as far as any congratulations were ever likely to go. After all, this child had not yet reached home.

Colin returned to the interview room where mother and daughter were beginning to emerge from the relief of their emotional reunion. They each expressed unanimous enthusiasm for trying again, with Sally's help, to restore a measure of equanimity. Colin, for his part, was not inclined to underestimate the scale of the task in hand though, as he intimated to each of them, but theirs was in no way an altogether exceptional state of family affairs.

"That's just how life can sometimes be for any of us. There are occasions when we just have to ask ourselves how we might best work through it," he said softly. "None of us are perfect."

Colin asked to use the telephone extension in the custody suite to report a summary of this outcome to Malcolm Miller, the duty senior. He concluded by saying that he would try to speak to the social worker, Sally, on Monday morning.

"That'll be Sally Hails," said Malcolm, in a reassuringly knowledgeable tone. "There's something else for you though on your way back."

"Okay," replied Colin. "What's to do?"

"Well, this is an unusual one," Malcolm explained, "could be right up your street though. It seems that two young women in Neston Street, right by Tadgate prison there, have been cavorting in an upstairs window – in full view of the prisoners opposite – engaged in some sort of striptease performance for the benefit of onlooking inmates. There's been chaos apparently. The particular wing of the prison is in lockdown, on the verge of riot. You see, told you it was right up your street!"

"Hmm, interesting," observed Colin, "but, er, what's all of that got to do with us? Unless of course they think you and I might be able to contribute anything to the show?"

"Not at all," Malcolm laughed. "Well not quite, but there is a complication. The two women involved have been arrested and taken into custody. They are likely, at the very least, to be charged with public order offences and inciting riot. And, here's the sting in the tail so to speak, one of them, Natalie Meyrick, aged eighteen, has a thirteen month-old infant. The women will be held overnight and this raises queries about the care of the child, Eloise. Two police women have remained at the property, temporarily taking charge of Eloise and – as you can imagine – they are eagerly awaiting your arrival."

"Oh, marvellous," exclaimed Colin. "I'll bet they are. Do we know of any other relatives?"

"Nothing known at all I'm afraid," confessed Malcolm, almost apologetically, "the police have been pretty tied up with it, alongside having to deal with a raft of other Saturday night priorities."

"I'll be about half an hour, but tell them I'll first be going to the 'nick' to speak to Natalie."

"I'll bet you will," said Malcolm, as he put the phone down.

This somewhat unusual set of circumstances surprisingly resulted, by contrast, in a run-of-the-mill sort of outcome. While Eloise was already subject to an ongoing assessment by social services because of general welfare concerns, the immediate crisis was resolved when the maternal grandmother came forward to take care of the child.

Colin was appreciably reassured by Eloise's beaming smile on being lifted up and caressed by someone who she clearly saw as a very familiar face. Hurriedly undertaken background checks of grandmother, and other members of her household, revealed no information to suggest they were in any way unfavourable temporary carers for this little girl. The unwelcome prospect of receiving yet another child into care that evening had fast abated, at least in the shorter term.

All of the conspiring implications concerning Eloise's future welfare, together with the outcome of police enquiries and of further aspects of parenting assessments, were subsequently evaluated in a case conference held some three weeks later. Unsurprisingly, social work support and further monitoring of Eloise's progress would remain firmly in place for the foreseeable future.

SIX

Sixes and sevens

DURING COLIN'S MONDAY MORNING drive to the Longley office, he could not help wondering about Gemma Graham and how the rest of the weekend might have gone for her and her family. Having spent much of the weekend basking in the glow of satisfaction in not receiving a child into care, he then agonised over the extent to which that reward might have merely been the product of an element of emotional blackmail.

Oh yes, he thought, pulling himself together, *mustn't forget to ring Sally Hails.*

As he drove along, bright spring sunshine illuminated the vivid, widespread urban decay blighting this district, and, what's more, the people who lived there. The emptiness of derelict factories and abandoned pit-heaps loomed large in reflections on the still water of the canal at Fenport. Colin inched his way slowly across the bridge, joining a long queue of traffic.

On reaching the office, the now-heaving car park contrasted starkly with its hollow emptiness on Friday. *That only seemed like yesterday*, Colin thought on entering office reception. Laden with work-related documents, he found a predictably busy, busy week already in full swing. Bubbling chatter almost drowned the competing shrills of more than one ringing telephone.

Pam and Karen's 'to-ing and fro-ing' were prominent within this hubbub of activity, along with other admin staff who worked at the beginning of the week. Pam, bless her, was still glowing with unabated excitement over Saturday's Grand National. For his part, however, Colin's distractions of being on emergency duty had somehow put that quite out of his mind. Moreover, he had not really committed much of it to memory anyway.

"Elizabeth Winstanley's won the 'sweep', with Ben Nevis," said Pam exuberantly, and still glowing. "Seven pounds first prize!"

"Who?" said Colin, furrowing his brow.

"Elizabeth," said Pam with a degree of emphasis. "She's the new social worker on Dennis's team. Come on, Colin, where've you been? She's been here a couple of weeks or more now."

At this, the penny dropped for Colin. The arrival of a new social worker had indeed been recently announced. For various reasons, however, including her appointment to another team, he had simply not yet had the opportunity to meet her.

"I think your two horses are still running, Colin," said Pam sarcastically.

Colin then made his way earnestly from reception. He had loads to do.

Apart from contacting Sally Hails, he remembered he had to return Jim Rathbone's call. Jim, the manager of the local day centre, was not someone who social workers were wise to keep waiting, let alone ignore completely. He also needed to discuss the Grattages with Cora, and furthermore, he had not yet had chance of even putting pen to paper in recording any of last week's visits.

He entered the Intake team room to find only Ivor Axford at his desk. Ivor, a social worker of considerable experience – harking back to his days as a childcare officer in the old Children's Department – was someone who Colin was inclined to look up to. Ivor appeared to be in telephone contact with the juvenile court officer. Their conversation appeared to relate to a teenager, known to Ivor, who was to appear in court that morning, following his arrest over the weekend in connection with what sounded like a string of burglaries.

As Colin promptly got down to business, Sally Hails had to be given first priority. He picked up the phone and dialled the Wrinley office, a telephone number he now knew off by heart.

"Blast!" he said, on finding that Sally was not in. So he rather unsatisfactorily left a message with an admin assistant, asking her to call back.

Jim Rathbone, on the other hand, always seemed to be in. He greeted Colin's call enthusiastically before promptly reminding him that he had put his name forward some time ago to assist on a forthcoming handicapped holiday.

This was a well-established and widely acclaimed annual week's holiday for the physically handicapped – as disabled people were then known – many of whom attended Jim's day centre. While Colin certainly had these holiday dates in his diary, he had subconsciously assumed the holiday was some weeks away.

Somewhat to Colin's dismay, Jim was brimming with the excitement of there being only two weeks to go before they were 'off'! Colin groaned. He could have well done without it given all of his other distractions. On the other hand, of course, he recognised the invaluable opportunity of this sort of experience. Colin was continuously alert to taking advantage of any opportunity to enhance his professional development.

Jim was inviting him over to explain precise expectations surrounding the necessary social work duties and responsibilities in managing this important event. Colin had yet to discover how the laborious detail of this forthcoming explanation was widely understood to be typical of Jim's exhaustively ponderous style. He accordingly agreed with Jim an opportunity for their meeting, though Colin had the distinct impression that Jim may have been expecting to see him much sooner.

Cora then came into the team room to speak with Ivor about the young man he had been discussing on the telephone. The local police inspector had simultaneously been taking the trouble of mentioning this lad's circumstances to Cora. He felt that this young tearaway, named Ellis, might somehow benefit from the sort of advice and assistance attributed to social workers that childcare legislation was so keen to emphasise. While Cora was not really sure whether the police inspector was being sarcastic in this vein, she responded with her characteristically good-natured exuberant air by saying that her staff would of course be pleased to see what could be done. She also thanked him for bringing this matter to her attention, and, at this point, any hint of sarcasm lay firmly with Cora.

As soon as she had relayed all of this to Ivor, Colin spied his chance. "Morning, Cora!" he said brightly. "Any chance I could have a word about the Grattages?"

"Come on through," she said in her familiar welcoming way, gesticulating to him to follow her into her office and inviting him to take a seat. No sooner were they seated at each side of Cora's desk than she promptly lit a cigarette. Her reputation for being fond of this particular full-strength brand preceded her far and wide. A plume of bluish smoke billowed above her head as she blew out the match.

Having taken this delayed opportunity of seeking the benefit of Cora's experience on what he regarded as a complex set of family circumstances, Colin suddenly realised that he had not at all rehearsed what he wanted to say. For what seemed to him like an awkward interval, he did not know where to begin, appearing lost for words. Cora did not prompt him in any way. She maintained her fixed gaze, albeit with eyes half-closed, peering through horizontal layers of hovering blue smoke.

"I don't seem to be making any headway with this family," Colin eventually blurted out. "Sometimes I can reassure myself that things are beginning to improve. Then, no sooner said than done, we're back to square one, almost predictably with a bump."

Having made this awkward start in explaining the Grattage problems, as he saw them, illustrating the haphazard way in which the family existed – devoid of any organisation – and how all of that appeared to affect each of them, six individuals no less, Colin's commentary gradually became more fluid. It simultaneously rose in pitch as the cumulative frustrations of being unable to effect any positive change again began to get the better of him.

"It sometimes feels like one step forward and two back," he said finally, awkwardly feeling that he was beginning to repeat himself.

"Hmm," Cora uttered pensively, stubbing out her cigarette as two parallel jets of smoke issued from her nostrils. As ash fell falteringly down the front of her tweed jacket, she leant forward asking quizzically. "Who's your closest ally in all of this?"

"Er, I suppose you are," Colin replied, somewhat feebly.

"No," said Cora emphatically. "Not me! While I'm mildly encouraged to hear you regard me as an ally, in terms of your interaction with clients I am perhaps rather more of a checkpoint-Charlie," she said with a grin.

"Who's your closest ally in your direct dealings with the family? It can sometimes be another family member or it could be any other person who happens to be in touch with the family concerned, including another professional. It inevitably has to be someone on the same wavelength as yourself, if you get my meaning, and with whom you might be in direct contact from time to time."

"Oh," Colin mused. "Viv Prosser, I suppose." This was the family's health visitor, who was based in the local health centre, situated next door to the Longley area office.

"Have you and Viv ever visited the family together?" Cora probed.

"Well, no," said Colin, though he followed this up by saying, "it's just that we sometimes discuss our findings and opinions with one another. We have consciously tried to avoid the impact of two professionals invading the family at the same time. Do you think we should be actually making joint-visits?"

"Not necessarily," said Cora, "though there could well be certain advantages in that from time to time, provided you were clear about what those advantages might be. No, I think we might go even one better than that. What about introducing Maggie Rushton to the family?"

Maggie was a popular, well-respected family-aide. This was someone who would often work alongside social workers by engaging in largely practical tasks with people in receipt of social work services. This could involve anything from simply providing transport to appointments and other functions on the one hand, to implementing programmes promoting people's independence by helping to manage aspects of their lives, on the other. It could extend, in some circumstances, to enhancing their parenting ability too, and, crucially, to the point of actually making a real difference in avoiding the trauma of family breakdown.

Family-aides, like Maggie, were largely seen – to some extent – as unqualified social workers. They would make up for any absence of academic qualification with shed-loads of untold experience of family life. Maggie, for her part, had worked for years in the textile industry. She was a mother and a grandmother in her early fifties, who, having raised her own children, worked in welfare services as a home help. She subsequently became a family aide on the advent of social services departments. The distinct merits of having people with proven life experience working alongside families far outweighed that of having eager young graduates haplessly articulating merely vague details of a troubled family's shortcomings.

Colin might have glibly admitted that he had not given a thought to the prospect of engaging a family aide on the Grattages' behalf. People like Maggie were few and far between. It was by no means uncommon for social workers' requests for a family aide to be summarily rejected out of hand on the basis of their being far too busy with established priorities. Now, however, it was being mooted by a senior social worker, indeed Cora Malone no less, which therefore made it a very different prospect.

"I'll give Maggie the nod," said Cora authoritatively, reaching casually in her top drawer for her cigarettes. "I'll ask her to make contact with you over the next couple of days."

Colin thanked her and made good his swift departure to get on with the rest of, what seemed, on the basis of this lift from Cora, a lightened load of things to do. His elation was short-lived, however. On his desk was a note asking him to call the duty officer at the Tadgate office 'urgently', concerning Eloise Meyrick.

Colin groaned. "Damn it," he muttered, "that should've been my second phone call this morning." Tadgate staff must have learned about the prison episode from another source. They would have been justified in wanting to know exactly why they had not heard about it directly from Colin, first thing that morning. He only realised at this point that he had left some of the documentation from his weekend duty stint in the admin office on his arrival that day. So he went downstairs to retrieve it.

The items he was looking for had already been very efficiently placed in his personalised pigeon-hole by admin staff, along with no less than six other 'please ring back' messages and items of in-coming post. As he quickly sifted through that bundle of papers, with his back towards the remainder of the busy office, he heard Karen addressing him.

"Colin, this is Elizabeth. She's the new social worker on Dennis's team."

Colin turned to find a tall, bespectacled woman in her mid-thirties holding out her hand to greet him. Colin promptly responded with a similarly outstretched hand, as Karen added in a slightly hushed tone, "It was Elizabeth who won first prize in the office sweepstake."

"Wow, congratulations, Liz," he retorted in an exaggeratedly enthusiastic vein. This may have been partly by way of mild surprise at just how elegant he thought she looked.

"It's Elizabeth, actually," the tall, elegant woman replied curtly, but still smiling.

"Oh, right," said Colin, a touch apologetically, and in that feeble way that had now affected him on more than one occasion that morning. He felt that he had been properly put in his place.

"I'm pleased to make your acquaintance, Elizabeth," he said hurriedly, with a slightly more assertive air. "Should you feel that I might be of any assistance in acquainting you with the local area, or by introducing you to certain contacts in other agencies, don't hesitate to ask," he added in a much more consoling way.

"Indeed I will," said Elizabeth with her fixed broad smile and an accompanying nod of her head in polite recognition. "Thank you very much. I'll be pleased to bear that in mind."

Colin turned swiftly on his heels to return to his desk in the sort of way that military discourse might have termed a tactical withdrawal from this assertive new colleague. *I wonder by what route she meandered into social work*, he thought to himself as he prepared to make his now well overdue contact with the Tadgate office.

In the event, that task was thankfully achieved in a relatively straightforward way. Colin of course liberally peppered his explanatory overview of what had evidently become generally known as 'the prison episode' with apologies for being somewhat delayed in getting back to them. There had been, he lamented, a host of other Monday morning distractions. Following a further handful of other administrative tasks, he was eventually able to turn his attention again to the matter of the Grattage household.

Colin was beginning to feel that they were somehow taking over his life – and not just his working life! He had, it had to be said, been trying to work with them for a considerable time now, somewhat exceeding the six to eight weeks that nominally accounted for Intake team involvement. Several factors, however, appeared to be causing this unduly prolonged attachment.

On one hand, the family had already endured a long sequence of different social workers, among a host of other well-intentioned and long-suffering professionals. Cora was trying hard to stem this unhelpful flow. In other respects, Colin had not really reached any tangible plateau of stability in family fortunes to be able to viably hand over casework responsibility to someone else. In any case, Cora might have argued that the Grattages were the sort of not untypical 'problem family' on whom Colin needed to effectively 'cut his teeth' during this embryonic stage of his professional development.

As he hurriedly signed-out in the office logbook to indicate his current destination, and almost in dread of bumping into Elizabeth Winstanley again, he began to turn his thoughts towards marshalling the focus of this imminent Grattage visit. Its aims and objectives had to go well beyond an update on matters arising, let alone the doubtful prospect of reporting tamely on any hope of progress. He would thankfully be able to commence in at least one positive vein in terms of the good news for the family having some practical help at home, courtesy of Maggie Rushton. This was assuming that June Grattage might share his optimism – let alone comprehend its real purpose.

He also remembered that Viv Prosser, the family health visitor, had recently managed to obtain a larger and newer pushchair on the family's behalf. The one in which young Terry Grattage was frequently seen was in a distinctly sorry state, having already served each of his older siblings. So Colin took a minor detour from the car park via the health centre nextdoor to collect the pushchair, and thereby securing what might hopefully be regarded by June as a second piece of good news.

At first sight, Sparrow Park Estate looked vaguely welcoming in the spring sunshine. By the time that Colin arrived in the cul-de-sac where Tommy and June lived, the forlorn state of the pathways – some strewn with abandoned toys, others vividly laid bare by missing gates – led commonly to equally forlorn front doors. This was for him now very familiar territory, void of any apparent sense of pride or of real belonging. It was strange, he thought, how this spectre of desolation can freely accommodate people who might genuinely be regarded as 'the salt of the earth' as well as others conforming – rightly or wrongly – to as many other discriminatory labels the wider public might muster.

Colin made his customary way to the Grattages' back-door. Front doors were seldom used on this estate, save largely for debt-collectors and bailiffs. He knocked fairly loudly, without trying to make it seem too much like officialdom, and pushed the door open, in a time-honoured way. June answered his knocking by appearing in the kitchen. She was dressed in a rollneck jumper and tweed trousers that Colin knew Viv Prosser had donated weeks ago. She had five-year-old Susan in tow. Terry, of course, still pushchair-bound, must have predictably been left to his own devices in the living room.

"Oh, hiya," she said passively. "I thought it might be you."

Colin entered without necessarily being invited inside. June seldom went as far as embarking on that sort of social intercourse.

"I've brought you another pushchair for Terry," Colin said by way of at least some form of introductory courtesy, "though it's actually from Viv Prosser. Hello there, Susan. It's a nice surprise seeing you," he added, bending down and smiling at Susan. The point he was making here, about Susan not being in school, was otherwise lost on those present. Colin held out a small packet of chocolate drops that Susan grabbed, before promptly turning away without saying anything. Colin decided to maintain this positive air by actively dismissing for now the familiar curtain-raiser of asking why Susan was not in school.

June's facial expression revealed a mild degree of pleasure, Colin thought, but she, like her daughter, otherwise said nothing in response. Colin did not really expect anything else. The kitchen was in its customary state of extensive clutter. It was difficult to imagine how, or indeed where, any food preparation might ever take place. There were a number of dirty dishes in and around the sink that looked as though they must have, at some time, contained sorts of food.

"Is Tommy in?" asked Colin enthusiastically.

"Na," June replied, still passively. "He's out with Riggo."

Colin almost warmed to this fleeting morsel of volunteered information. Riggo was someone who Colin would hear of generally around the estate, but who was otherwise – as far as he could tell – unknown to him.

"Shall we go and find Terry?" Colin asked, holding out his hand in inviting June to lead the way. Terry was inevitably sitting vacantly in his pushchair. He looked up expressionless at the three people entering the room, bearing in mind that two of them were familiar to him. Colin thought that he at least looked well-nourished. He was much less sure, however, about what progress he might be making – at ten months – in beginning to move around independently or even in his being able to sit-up by himself.

"Does Terry move about much on the floor?" Colin asked in an enthusiastic tone.

"Yeah, a bit," June replied in the same monotonously passive tone, lifting her son from the pushchair before placing him on the grubby carpet square and propping his back against an easy chair. She handed him a soft toy elephant that Terry grasped in earnest. He turned it over in his hands, examining it intently.

Colin bent down to speak to Terry in an appropriately friendly way. Terry glanced fleetingly in response before returning his gaze to the much more interesting toy elephant before toppling over sideways. He then made limited efforts to push himself up from his prone position on the floor. He began to whimper. While Susan promptly picked up the elephant, June lifted Terry and cuddled him, somewhat to Colin's mild relief. In every other respect, however, Terry's overall development remained a distinctly uncertain aspect of his welfare.

"I'm sorry Tommy's not in," Colin proffered, in the sort of tone suggestive of a change of subject. June, however, somewhat encouragingly maintained her focus on Terry. "We've been wondering about providing some extra support for you at home," he continued, "but we wouldn't do anything like that unless you were agreeable to it. What do you think?"

"Yeah, that would be all right I suppose," replied June in a continuingly passive vein.

"But Tommy would also need to be happy with it," Colin added.

"Huh, he won't mind," June replied, with a toss of her head. "He's hardly ever here." Probably without realising it, she was effectively confirming what Colin had strongly suspected all along – that June was left to contend with housework, childcare and virtually all other family commitments single-handedly.

"He still needs to be okay with it though," Colin emphasised. He went on to mention Maggie by name and to explain something of her role in working *with* June – rather than *for* her – in establishing domestic routines. This would involve him and Maggie agreeing with June, and of course with Tommy as well, about priorities. Many of those would necessarily focus on the children. And in doing so, he again stressed the important role that Dawn, as the oldest child, should not be overlooked. He was not at all sure though that June was able to appreciate this nuance.

"I'd like to bring Maggie round next week to introduce her to you both," said Colin kindly, trying to maintain this positive, constructive tone. He therefore, with somewhat mixed feelings, again dismissed the more searching question of why Susan was not in school. Despite thinking this may be little short of a flagrant cop-out, his parting shot to June was merely that of saying, "I'll see you next week then, and hopefully introduce you both to Maggie."

SEVEN

The science of uncertainty

TODAY SAW COLIN ON office duty. He would be one of two social workers from the Intake team fielding incoming calls or interviewing people visiting the area office to seek assistance. The specific role of duty officers ranged widely from merely giving one-off advice to gathering information prior to any subsequent assessment being undertaken. That follow up would incorporate further short-term help on an ongoing basis in any given set of circumstances.

Individual duty officers would themselves determine how they might share emerging priorities during the course of their shift. One would usually be the first point of telephone contact, while the other worker might field calls when their colleague was otherwise engaged or take responsibility for making visits away from the office to deal with more pressing 'referrals', as these requests for help were known.

So, Colin had to be early into work. For once, his was one of only a handful of cars in the office car park first thing that morning. Admin staff were always in early, so was Cora Malone. It occurred to him though that he would not necessarily recognise the vehicle belonging to the formidable Elizabeth Winstanley.

Must not be off-guard in bumping into the redoubtable Elizabeth this morning, Colin thought as he reversed his red Triumph into a favoured spot. However, he could not yet see Ivor Axford's car. Ivor would be the other duty officer that day and he was not necessarily someone who had a reputation for being, like Colin, a generally late starter.

Ivor's experience, certainly in terms of childcare matters, was a 'big plus' for the Intake team. He would therefore be a considerable source of reassurance for Colin during their duty, particularly if Cora had to go out. On the other hand, while Ivor was not exactly lazy, he was well known, through the maturity of well-rehearsed persuasion, to articulate any number of reasons for his not taking on a particular case, or in arguing why he might not be exactly the right man for a task.

"Hmm…" Colin murmured to himself as he pushed open the office door, "I wonder if Ivor might manage to shove anything my way today."

He went fittingly, like a proverbial homing pigeon, to his office pigeon-hole to pick up messages and any incoming post. He was, perhaps subconsciously, on a mission to avoid Elizabeth again. On top of the handful of papers he retrieved from the pigeon-hole was a note in Cora's unmistakable hand. It had been written, for goodness sake, at ten to eight that morning!

Colin grimaced upon realising it concerned a well-known – if not a well-regarded – client, the infamous Eileen Agnew no less, whose ubiquitous reputation went well before her. She was in her early fifties and had been well known to the mental health department for many years prior to the reorganisation heralding the advent of social services departments.

To what extent Eileen was mentally ill in diagnostic terms, was not absolutely clear, though she had acquired that label on often having been sectioned under the Mental Health Act. Any number of those episodes had resulted in her being consigned compulsorily to a psychiatric hospital. Each of those occasions would have been almost routinely generated by Eileen's propensity towards episodes of irrational, bizarre and sometimes violent behaviour.

Eileen had also spent her later childhood in a mental handicap hospital, for patients having what would have subsequently been seen as mental disability, though again, to what extent she might have then had any discernible disability was similarly questionable. She perhaps might have been more readily regarded as what later became known as a 'sociopath' though Eileen probably defied any realistic professional label. Eileen was well, simply Eileen. It may have been partly this distinct absence of any broad 'diagnosis' that precluded staff from any professional background being able to find a sustainable, long-term solution to bring lasting stability to Eileen's eventful life. That remote perspective remained a perpetual challenge for all concerned – and not least for poor Eileen.

She was therefore – shamefully Colin thought – systematically passed around the local authority, on a cyclical basis for goodness sake, between specified residential units that provided various services for adults who had additional, identified needs. In this way, each unit was required to take its turn in enduring the somewhat mixed blessing of looking after Eileen on a short-term basis. Those catering variously for elderly people, and those providing support to people recovering from mental illness, were specifically included in contributing to a planned accommodation schedule. This was spelled out on a six to eight week cycle. Eileen was effectively of no fixed abode.

Furthermore, that planned schedule could be suddenly curtailed upon Eileen precipitating an unanticipated crisis, characteristically via another episode of extreme behaviour. The acute distress potentially caused by such outbursts to other vulnerable residents would be routinely cited volubly and at length by any responsible unit manager in an attempt to persuade senior managers to promptly move Eileen on again. This would variously be to 'somewhere else', irrespective of what the formal schedule might have decreed and irrespective of Eileen's choice.

It was coincidentally one such crisis that had led to Cora's note to Colin on this particular morning. The previous evening, emergency duty staff had been involved in removing Eileen from a mental health hostel in another locality, following her familiar altercation with another resident. She had allegedly reacted violently to the other resident volubly protesting at Eileen flagrantly taking their milk from the fridge. Irrespective of whether Eileen might have any remote idea about any such courtesies, it had resulted in a number of plates being smashed in the kitchen. This somewhat fittingly added significantly to an evolving spectre of late-night drama. It also led to Eileen haplessly having to move on again.

For the duty social worker, the given task was said to be little more than that of transporting Eileen to Scotch Corner Lodge, a homeless persons' unit situated within the Longley locality. Scotch Corner was indeed written boldly into the infamous Eileen Agnew 'schedule'. While Scotch Corner was not due to receive Eileen again for another two or three weeks, they happened to have a vacancy – so, it was off to Scotch Corner she promptly went. Crisis over!

More to the point, however, since Eileen had previously been known to Colin in very similar circumstances, Cora's note requested he make contact with Scotch Corner staff and keep in touch with them for the duration of Eileen's current stay.

"Morning then, Colin," said Pam sarcastically, in eventually retrieving him from this engrossed scrutiny of various messages. He returned her greeting in his characteristically hearty way, mumbling a fleeting apology.

"Your unusually early start this morning somehow tells me you might be on duty?" Pam sighed, maintaining her sarcastic tone. "Am I right?"

"Okay, Pam, game over. Can we change the subject?" Colin said, in his continuing good-natured vein. In then returning to the business of the day, he asked, "Anything good happening yet?"

"Not really," Pam replied flatly. "Cora's spoken to last night's duty worker though."

"Yes, tell me about it," replied Colin, returning Pam's sarcasm, as he strode towards the door. "Latest news is that Eileen Agnew's back on our patch. Hold the front page!"

On leaving the admin office, Colin virtually bumped into the incoming Maggie Rushton. "Oh, morning, Maggie," he said, somewhat startled. "Er, I don't suppose Cora's happened to have had a word with you yet?"

"Indeed she has," replied Maggie, with a glowing smile. "Do we need to make an introductory visit somewhere in the vicinity of Sparrow Park?"

"We certainly do," said Colin, reassured that Cora had not wasted any time in making this connection with Maggie about the Grattage family. "I can't do anything today 'cos I'm on duty. I could do tomorrow though, after the allocation meeting, if that were to suit you?"

"Tomorrow's fine," said Maggie. "Come and find me somewhere around my desk any time after half-eleven."

As it turned out, this particular duty session got off to an unusually slow start. Ivor and Colin each fielded a few largely 'information only' calls from other agencies and the odd routine request for elderly and 'handicapped' people – as people with disabilities were then known – to be issued with disability aids.

Then, come late morning, it all changed. The phones went mad. Ivor had meanwhile become absorbed by an escalating crisis concerning one of his own cases. It apparently began to consume him amid a series of formidably long telephone conversations.

While Colin was still busily writing up referrals summarising action already taken on certain matters, his phone rang again. Karen's familiar voice from the switchboard announced that a Mrs Frances Healey was on the line, the head teacher from Eversleigh nursery school. "It's about a child named Sarah McNally, from Justing Street, but who doesn't appear to be known to us," Karen announced.

"Okay," said Colin. "Put her through." He promptly introduced himself to the caller.

"I'm ringing about a four-year-old named Sarah McNally who has been with us since the beginning of this term," announced Mrs Healey in what Colin thought an unusually hesitant way for a head teacher. "Staff are used to seeing Mum in school," she added, "but Sarah is somewhat behind for her age, particularly in speech and language, and that's something we are working on."

"Are parents on board in addressing those difficulties?" Colin enquired enthusiastically.

"Well, sort of," the head replied, "but Mum herself is not really very bright and we don't know much about her. While she's pleasant enough, she's not particularly forthcoming in any conversational way."

"Okay," said Colin, "go on."

"Well, we understand that Sarah's parents have recently separated. Dad has moved out, we don't know exactly where to, but not far away," Mrs Healey continued.

"We know little about him either; he's someone we rarely see."

"So," said Colin, interjecting on what seemed like a pregnant pause, "how do you anticipate that we might help in any of this?"

"Well," replied Mrs Healey, clearing her throat, "this is a little bit tricky. We understand that Sarah has had contact with her dad some of the time during last weekend. And, well, she's not been at all herself today. She's been quite tearful and…" There was another pause. "…well, saying things that give us some concern."

"Go on," said Colin, in as neutral a way as he could muster.

"Well," the head teacher reiterated, still somewhat hesitantly. "She's been making several references to what I can only describe as 'Daddy's dickie' and then she becomes all upset again. It's very worrying and we are unsure what to do. I've spoken to a head teacher colleague from another school and they have said we should report this to social services."

"Okay," said Colin, "fair enough. That could well be the correct advice, but let's put together as much initial information as we may have. At risk of asking naively obvious questions, what do you regard as the basis of your concern? Might references to 'dickie' be something unusual for kids in your school?"

"I should say so," exclaimed Mrs Healey. "We do not encourage that sort of language in school! This child is in a state of acute distress!" Her tone became much more assertive.

"Of course," said Colin, "that's to be expected." But he simultaneously thought to himself how children of that age can become innocently fascinated with physical differences between boys and girls. He was also aware of research evidence that indicated a significant proportion of children under the age of five might occasionally see their parents in various states of undress. It was a proportion, however, that significantly decreased as children became older. So, he thought, it may not necessarily be such a big deal, without daring to make this observation explicitly to Mrs Healey.

That said, he thought to himself, feeling at risk of coming under fire from this head teacher with what he was inclined to say. *It's important to start with what we have. What we have here is a senior professional from another agency expressing real concern about a child. It's also important to hang on to what you have and to avoid making any sort of premature assumptions.*

In returning to the matter in hand, he asked, "Who are you expecting to collect Sarah from school today?"

"Mum, of course," came the prompt and still assertive reply.

"What time would that be?" asked Colin, actively trying to remain calm and collected and avoiding any sort of bristling resentment to this question-and-answer dialogue from the other end of the line.

"She'll be here before three o'clock," said Mrs Healey.

"Leave this with me for now, Mrs Healey. I'll need to check a couple of things before getting back to you in determining what action we will be taking."

"How long is *that* likely to take?" she asked dryly.

"Not long," Colin said cheerily. "It will be well within the next half-hour. I'll get back to you soon," he chimed positively, before ringing off.

The next half-hour that he'd stoically promised did not get off to a good start at all. Referrals about child abuse, or even suspected abuse – in the wake of little Maria – inevitably demanded certain expectations of action to be taken by local authorities to leave no stones unturned. First among these in this particular authority was that initial visits by a social worker should be conducted jointly with the respective senior social worker in ensuring that a thorough assessment is undertaken.

Colin, therefore, went dutifully to find Cora in accord with these expectations. "She's gone out," chirped Pam, upon his enquiry in the admin office. "IT meeting, I think. She won't be back until late afternoon." He went immediately to find Ivor, who would undoubtedly be seen as a worthy deputy for Cora in these circumstances.

"No can do, Teach," Ivor said promptly with a wave of his hand, before Colin had embarked on any sort of overview to his request. 'Teach', incidentally, was Ivor's nickname for Colin, apparently reflecting his previous employment in education. Somewhat less clear was the extent to which it was a friendly term or rather a sarcastic pun. "See if Annie might go with you," Ivor added by way of an uninterested, almost throwaway afterthought.

Annie Wrigley was another experienced and well-regarded member of the Intake team, though her background was in Welfare Services rather than in childcare. "Yes, of course I'll go with you," said Annie. Her obliging agreement was uttered even before Colin had begun to convey the whole picture. "It might also be worth putting Jean Whitehead on alert, just in case," Annie added.

This is just the sort of wisdom that is required, Colin thought to himself in acting on Annie's suggestion. Her involvement already seemed to be really paying dividends. Jean Whitehead was an experienced detective constable with many years' service. She was also something of an exception among dyed-in-the-wool CID networks, in that she had fostered fond and effective working relationships with staff in fledgling social services departments.

Much of Jean's established rapport with Longley's social workers had been forged way back, having first become acquainted with the likes of Cora and Ivor in Childeren's Department days. Colin's hurried call, however, to DC. Whitehead was very short and sweet. It was yet another anti-climax. She was on leave. There was no one else in CID who Colin really knew, so he politely declined the offer to speak to someone else.

He instead double-checked with Karen that none of the names or addresses given in relation to Sarah McNally's family was previously known to the local authority. Indeed, they were not, apparently. Experience, however, sometimes tended to show that this sort of sweeping denial did not necessarily bring with it any cast-iron guarantees.

He rang Mrs Healey back, outlining the limited background he had mustered and said that he and his colleague Annie Wrigley would be arriving in school within the next half-hour. "It will be well before three o'clock, of course?" Mrs Healey asked searchingly, in a continuingly cynical tone.

"Yes, it will," Colin said confidently. "We are virtually on our way."

Eversleigh nursery school was little over a mile from the office. As Colin got out of his car, however, it suddenly dawned on him that he and Annie had not at all discussed how they were going to manage the collection of information that would be imminently required. This was as serious as it gets in critical assessment terms. Who would first speak to whom? How would he and Annie coordinate their respective roles? Who would take the lead in speaking to a four-year-old? At what point might it become necessary to inform the police? Fortunately, at least the first part would be easy – by merely asking for Mrs Healey. They'd simply just have to take it from there.

The two social workers were shown through to Mrs Healey's office. It was not nearly as spacious as Colin was expecting. Mrs Healey, instantly identifiable with her hair tied back tightly in a bun and dressed smartly in a grey two-piece suit, held her hand out warmly to greet them. Also present was a small child, who Colin correctly assumed to be Sarah McNally, sitting on the lap of a member of staff, who turned out to be Sarah's class teacher.

Colin was immediately struck by how overwhelming four adults, two of them complete strangers, must have seemed to this little girl. Sarah's gaze was unsurprisingly fixed towards the floor. She was sucking her thumb.

"Hello, Sarah," Colin said valiantly and with a broad smile, though she did not look up. "We are pleased to see you." Still no response, beyond Sarah fidgeting nervously on the teacher's lap. She avidly avoided Colin by any means. He, in turn, was immediately struck by the somewhat clumsy nature of his opening remarks to the child.

"This lady and gentleman have come to talk to you, Sarah, about what might be making you so upset," Mrs Healey interjected. This was met with yet more silent fidgeting.

"We may need to find ways of helping Sarah to feel more at ease," Annie suggested by way of an aside. "Small children tend to share more information voluntarily when their attention is otherwise engaged with something familiar – like a toy, or drawing a picture, or playing in the sandpit." This sensible suggestion, however, was suddenly interrupted by a knock at the office door.

Mrs Healey opened the door only slightly, saying firmly to the anonymous caller, "Not now. I'm dealing with something important."

"I know, Mrs Healey," the caller said confidently, "but this may be relevant to the matter in hand." Whereupon the head teacher managed to squeeze through the most limited space she had allowed herself to exit the door to speak to the caller in confidence. Colin, for his part, then felt inclined to join in Sarah's fidgeting as he began to endure what seemed like an endless vacant pause created by Mrs Healey's brief absence.

This was eventually broken when Mrs Healey returned to her office with an apparent air of relief. "Will you take

Sarah back to the classroom please, Mrs Mottram?" she said quietly. Mrs Mottram promptly followed this instruction without a word. Sarah, holding the teacher's hand, became suddenly energised enough to run alongside Mrs Mottram in making good her escape from this ordeal of grown-ups. Colin and Annie exchanged puzzled expressions.

"The cause of Sarah's distress," Mrs Healey announced almost triumphantly, "has apparently been solved when one of our domestics arrived in school this afternoon." Colin detected an air of muted glee in her tone as he and Annie looked on expectantly. "Our domestic apparently knows the family fairly well. Sarah's daddy apparently has – or at least did have – a little dog, a Jack Russell, named Dickie. The dog it seems was unfortunately run over at the weekend and Sarah has understandably been extremely upset about it."

A corporate sigh of relief from the two social workers was almost audible. "Crikey," was all that Colin could say in response.

"I'm really sorry to have bothered you over what can only be regarded as a misunderstanding," Mrs Healey said in a now more agreeable vein.

"Think no more about it," Annie replied obligingly, "though I'm sure you can understand that we will need to check all this out in reaching any sort of authoritative conclusion."

"Yes, of course," Mrs Healey said kindly. "By all means let me know if I may be of any further help." Colin felt that the erstwhile bristling head teacher was at risk of almost becoming a supportive colleague.

"Well, what do you make of all that?" Colin sighed on returning to his car. Annie was still somewhat speechless. She merely grimaced. As Colin clicked his seatbelt, he happened to notice Doris Betts's bleached-blonde neighbour, Natalie, chatting to other mums just inside the nursery yard.

"Just think," said Annie at last, "in any other circumstances that child's father could have been arrested at work and sitting in a cell waiting to be interviewed by now. Then what would we have said to him?" That harsh reality did not bear thinking about. They returned to the office in a somewhat silent state of shock.

News of this remarkable outcome had somehow reverberated around the office before Colin and Annie had found time to debrief. Cora had still not returned from her meeting, while Ivor, having initially marvelled at what he regarded as a most amusing outcome, was otherwise much too busy on other things to afford his colleagues any time in helping them to think through their experience in a constructive way.

The aftermath of it all would need to await a new dawn. Colin had no capacity to contemplate anything else that day. As he made his way to the car park, deep in thought in beginning to decide on the next likely steps, he was distracted by an unfamiliar voice. "Been hearing about some real ups and downs on the child abuse front," it announced.

Colin swung round to see Elizabeth Winstanley following him through the door. "Not half," he said with feeling. "It was a really close call on the acute embarrassment front too. How've you got to hear about it?"

"It's the sort of news that travels fast. It could well make the evening papers," Elizabeth replied sarcastically. "It just goes to show how we can't take anything for granted, I suppose. And after all, we should know by now that whatever it is that we try to do, we're damned when we do it and damned when we don't." She again tipped her head to one side, beaming that familiar warm smile. Colin took this to be a sympathetic and supportive gesture that had otherwise found him again stuck for words with this colleague.

"Not half," he eventually found himself spluttering nervously yet again. In collecting himself together, however, he was able to conclude how the episode had been a potent reminder of avoiding speculative assumptions if ever there was one. He then turned quickly on his heels and headed towards his car. "See you anon," he uttered over his shoulder in finally making good his getaway. Maybe she was not the forcefully aloof person he had originally assumed after all.

EIGHT

Fight or flight?

THE INTAKE TEAM'S WEEKLY allocation meeting provided more than just an opportunity for Cora to distribute cases for further intervention. It was also a forum for sharing new information about the organisation, including news of very occasional in-service training programmes. It highlighted professional matters arising from wider social work networks and, of course, extended to local gossip.

All of this forged common bonds and genuine interest among colleagues that led to the team gradually acquiring a general knowledge of one another's families and their interests away from work. It all contributed towards an acquisition of fluid team cohesion that effortlessly eclipsed any fabricated attempts at team building that later became a familiar quirk of organisational development.

On this particular morning, as team members began to assemble, Cora was recounting an amusing anecdote from the police inspector at Longley police station. He had been talking about a recently assigned young dog handler, who, having just arrived for an 'early' shift during the course of that week, had promptly received a call from officers still on the night shift.

They were acting on suspicions of intruders in the local Woolworths. The handler, with his dog of course, duly arrived on scene to promptly release the dog through the damaged front door of the premises. In these circumstances, police dogs were trained to head directly to the rear of a store before returning systematically via each of the aisles, between the displays, to locate and apprehend any intruder they might encounter.

Unfortunately, however, on this occasion, the police dog didn't get any further than the tail-wagging delights of the pick 'n' mix chocolate and toffee display! The whole of the station was still reeling over it. Even the handler, of course, was also able to appreciate its funny side, even in the absence of any sort of crime-busting result.

The real business of the day was about to begin, when Glenda Kirby, another member of the team, hurried into the meeting with a shopping bag. Glenda was a jolly, red-faced woman whose career in social work was driven by a genuine commitment towards the welfare of others. There was perhaps a certain puritanical element to this commitment, and even an almost patronising motivation in Glenda's charity towards those who she saw as less fortunate than herself. She was also, apparently, 'very big in church'. That said, Glenda was fairly big in most other areas too, and not just her generosity of spirit.

Glenda reached triumphantly into her bag to lift a pile of several rounds of bacon and cheese sandwiches, purchased still warm from the local Boulevard Café. These were promptly handed round the assembled circle of staff, which got the meeting off to a jolly good start. This pleased Cora in more ways than one, incidentally, since those with mouths full of sandwich were less able to articulate any feeble excuses on being handed any undesirable task or particularly challenging case.

Colin, however, was suitably encouraged from the outset on hearing Cora's announcement to the team that he would not be receiving any new cases from this meeting, because of his impending deployment to the forthcoming handicapped holiday. Furthermore, she explained, Colin had already resumed responsibility for the recently arrived Eileen Agnew, together with the follow-up to the now widely acclaimed circumstances of young Sarah McNally.

Mere mention of the handicapped holiday predictably prompted muted cheering among the team, since the highs and lows of that experience for unsuspecting social workers were well-known. Ivor Axford, from the more remote wisdom of his childcare background, spoke first by using this opportunity to query – in his familiar and all-knowing 'holier than thou' sort of way – the merits of social workers being used as cheap labour in these questionable excursions.

Cora, however, took this jibe effortlessly in her stride by suggesting that Ivor should feel free to volunteer himself on some subsequent occasion. He would then be able to report back authoritatively on the value, or indeed otherwise, of these experiences. She went on to extol the versatility of social work roles more seriously, emphasising the importance of staff resisting temptations to distance themselves from real people in arrogant sorts of ways that overt professionalism carelessly disregards.

"It's the people business that we're in," she emphasised with feeling. "It's not all that long ago," she went on, "during the miners' strike and the infamous three-day week, that the unassuming versatility of social workers was tested to its limit. They were then not infrequently required to fill coal sacks down at Fenport coal wharf, before distributing fuel to needy families on their caseloads."

The meeting was left to ponder that in a hushed, fleeting pause, with some perhaps ruminating about how widespread disquiet within the coal industry was far from over. The silence was broken by Annie Wrigley, trying to change the subject by asking Colin, out of genuine interest, how Eileen Agnew's recent arrival back in Longley was working out. "Err… I've not had chance to make contact with her yet," he had to confess. "What with one thing and another."

"That will have to be one of today's priorities then," Cora interjected, with yet another serious, knowing nod.

"Yes," Colin acknowledged, though he managed to avoid any insolent reference to it being just one of many.

When the allocation meeting dispersed nearly two hours later, with its business done, Colin went to find Maggie Rushton. He asked if they might delay their joint visit to the Grattage family until after lunch, since he had an Eileen Agnew matter to deal with. "Enough said," replied

Maggie with a grin. "It suits me actually," she added. "I'll meet you downstairs just after 2pm, if that's okay?"

"That's fine," replied Colin gladly. "See you then," he said, as he made his way swiftly to the car park, on his way at last to Scotch Corner Lodge.

The Lodge had been a homeless families' unit from the days when the old Welfare Department had responsibility for people in such circumstances. While that statutory duty had subsequently and more appropriately passed to housing departments, social services departments continued to have considerable input with people living there.

Social workers would often be working with families at Scotch Corner by trying to redress the impact of poverty – as a recurring burden among many – on the familiar pressures of family life. Much of that work would attempt to help families establish daily routines in budgeting and in effectively meeting the needs of children, by promoting at least some measure of domestic cohesion.

Staff working at the Lodge became relatively well known to Colin. They occupied a building containing administrative offices and other rooms where direct work could be undertaken with families to promote social and domestic skills, bearing in mind, of course, that much of that work would in any case take place in people's own flats. These were contained in a condominium of three modern blocks occupying the remainder of the Scotch Corner site. It was, therefore, to the office that Colin duly made his way in enquiring how things were progressing on Eileen's behalf.

"Oh, she's out," Brian Ramshorn announced, in

answer to Colin's query, but in a way that somehow implied that this was to everyone's satisfaction, including Eileen's. "She's otherwise kept herself very much to herself. She doesn't mix with anybody, not even staff – though we do try."

"Hmm…" murmured Colin. "It's early days. The bigger test will likely come when she has no money."

"The duty social worker, who brought her, actually left us with a sum of money from her benefit entitlement," said Brian. "We're letting her have some on a daily basis. So far, so good."

"The fun will come when it runs out," observed Colin, "unless we can get that sorted quickly with social security. They do not necessarily see Eileen as a priority case in the way that we do."

"The fun came," Brian suggested in an exaggerated way, "before she ever arrived here, no mistake. When the duty social worker accompanying her stopped at traffic lights en route, Eileen quickly got out of his car and hurriedly shoved her knickers down to her ankles, before stooping to urinate in the gutter. She was still in full flow, so-to-speak, when the lights changed. Vehicles behind were sounding their horns in all sorts of commotion, but Eileen, as ever, remained quite unperturbed. She never batted an eyelid in finishing the task in hand apparently, before nonchalantly getting back into the car."

"Good God," was all that Colin could initially muster in response. "She never ceases to amaze and that's no mistake." After chatting further with Brian over a handful of other administrative matters, he concluded that there was little else to do in Eileen's absence and that he would return later, after speaking with social security.

The next priority was that of meeting up with Maggie Rushton and introducing her to the Grattages. It only occurred to Colin as they were driving to Sparrow Park, that he had not really explained to Maggie the nature and extent of the family's problems, nor the things that he envisaged needed to be done in addressing them. His all-too-brief summary of their circumstances centred on how June's doubtless love of her kids dismally failed to materialise into anything like applied parenthood.

For Maggie, none of this was unfamiliar. She had heard it all before. It was only the names that tended to change. Nonetheless, she listened attentively to Colin's overview, nodding and smiling at each episode of the commentary that defined the family's chronic need.

Colin led the way up the path to the Grattages' back door, weaving between discarded items, including a child's sodden trainer. He knocked, as usual, before gently pushing the door open but without making the presumption of stepping inside unannounced. To his surprise, it was Tommy who came through to the cluttered kitchen.

"Oh, hello, Tommy," Colin chirped enthusiastically. "Good to see you." There was no response. "I've brought my colleague, Maggie, along to meet you," Colin added. "Did June happen to mention we'd be coming?"

There was still no response from Tommy. He stood motionless, staring at Colin. "Is it okay for us to come in?" Colin continued in this enthusiastic vein.

"No. Yer can get out," retorted Tommy solemnly. "Go

on, just get out."

"Is something the matter?" Colin asked, showing genuine concern that something may be amiss, just as June appeared in the hallway.

"Yes, you are," Tommy said in a more threatening tone. "Just get out, both of you, and if either of you as much as smirk, I'll slit your throat from ear to ear."

Colin felt distinctly weak at the knees. His immediate thought, however, was for Maggie's safety and how he might best protect her from any overt physical threat. It caused him to wonder if it was Maggie's arrival that had somehow upset Tommy in this way. Colin's next thought moved him to make up his mind, in the event of Tommy making any hurried move towards them, just where – and how hard – he would have to hit him in making good their escape.

Maggie, however, quietly composed, intervened at this point. "It's okay, Tommy," she said softly. "We are on our way. Today is obviously not a good time." Thereupon, she turned to leave, beckoning Colin to follow, though Colin – who was in no way of a violent disposition – had still not quite made up his mind whether fight or flight was necessarily going to be the order of the day.

On returning to the car, they momentarily sat silently, trying to pull themselves together from this unnerving experience. "Phew," Colin eventually exclaimed. "Whatever was that all about?"

"We may never know," Maggie replied, "but more to the point is what your next move is likely to be." Colin mused thoughtfully on this very valid point for much of their forlorn return to the office. He remained stunned, and indeed perplexed, in more ways than one, about what might have caused this unfamiliar reaction from Tommy Grattage.

Having dropped Maggie off with a low-key "I'll be in touch" cheerio, Colin went in search of Cora to relay details of this disconcerting episode. Almost predictably, however, Cora was out – at a management meeting no less – raising doubts about when, or whether, she would return that day. He was not inclined to seek solace from any other member of his team, nor to confide in any of the other senior social workers, bearing in mind, of course, that they were also likely to be at the management meeting. In any case, Colin mused, Maggie should be part of any debrief about what had taken place.

Moreover, he still had unresolved business on the Eileen Agnew front. Colin first called into the office on his arrival at Scotch Corner Lodge, to check with staff on any updates concerning Eileen. There weren't any. "She's in though," announced Nora, one of the supervisory staff. "Came in about an hour ago," she added, "but we've not really seen much of her today." At this, Colin promptly made his way across the lawn towards the block containing Eileen's flat.

He tapped on the door and could hear the television inside. There was no response, so he knocked louder. Still no response. He knocked again, this time announcing his name in a reasonably loud voice. Nothing. He stood back from the door to see if he could see any sign of life. There was still nothing. At this, Colin ambled back towards the office, looking in vain over his shoulder along the way.

"Looks as though she's in," he said to Nora, "but she's not answering the door."

"That's not at all unusual for Eileen," Nora replied passively. "She will make herself known though, when she wants something. I wouldn't worry too much about it."

"I've spoken to social security about her more recent change of address again, and they have assured me that it's all in hand," Colin said.

"That could well be a first. We'll see," Nora replied plaintively, "but don't you worry about that. We'll chase it." Colin expressed thanks for this encouraging team effort, whereupon there was a knock at the office door. Nora opened it to reveal Eileen standing there motionless.

Colin and Nora greeted her simultaneously in a sincerely welcoming chorus. Eileen said nothing in response, merely looking on with a sombre expression. Then, following a brief pause, she uttered in her gruff, stuttering voice that sounded almost like a growl, "M-Mr Millwood, c-c-can you come to my t-t-television?"

"What's the matter with it?" Colin asked with a degree of genuine concern. "Isn't it working?"

Eileen said nothing at first, before uttering, "Th-th-there's cookin' on b-both sides," referring here to the two main TV channels, BBC and ITV.

"Oh, Eileen," Nora interjected, "go back across and make yourself a cup of tea. By the time it's brewed, there will very likely be other programmes coming on."

Eileen, however, ignored this evidently superfluous remark. She was looking for immediate satisfaction. "C-c-can't you get 'em ter p-put a film on?" she asked, looking directly at Colin. "A-a wouldn't mind if it was a b-bloody cowboy," she added, stoically serious, by way of compromise.

Colin was much impressed with the influence Eileen evidently felt he had in the broadcasting world. On this basis at least, he could not disappoint her. So, he duly accompanied her back to her flat, resigned to what was likely to be a one-way conversation, as indeed it was, in premises that looked like no one lived there. Colin promptly took charge of making tea for two. What's more, his patience was rewarded – almost right on cue – by the television.

One of the culinary programmes was apparently edging towards its close – with chef happily wishing viewers well with their forthcoming delicacies. This was then to be followed, fortuitously no less, by the afternoon repertoire of children's TV. This, of course, was right up Eileen's street, as she happily settled down in earnest to watch a convenient cartoon with her mug of tea. It was thereby game over. Colin gladly took due credit in Eileen's evident, but unspoken, admiration for effecting this welcome change in fortunes.

On the downside, however, Colin unfortunately elected to bask in the relative rapture of this dubious success at the expense of addressing with Eileen some of the more substantial issues affecting her recent arrival at Scotch Corner. It was now well past 5pm. Colin meandered slowly home deep in thought. It had certainly been a day of contrasts. While reports of social workers being threatened – or worse – were by no means unheard of, this episode with Tommy had definitely been a first for Colin. It largely occupied his mind all evening, as he reflected upon it time and again.

Perhaps the worst of it was somehow interpreting it all as a failure on his part, a public failure no less, in front of a respected colleague, if not other onlookers. Did the whole of this event convey to Maggie that he had not made a proper assessment, that he had not even properly thought all this through? More compellingly, however, what next? How would he begin to negotiate contact with the Grattages now? This was not just a matter of losing face, nor was ceasing contact with them any sort of responsible option. He would, of course, be advised by Cora. That was it. She, if anyone, would help to determine his next steps.

NINE

Acquiring professional maturity

IT WAS NO GOOD. Colin couldn't leave it like that. Having spent an unsettled night ruminating over what he now regarded as a Grattage fiasco, there was only one thing for it. There was neither advice nor guidance required from Cora, nor indeed from anyone else for that matter. He had to go back to confront Tommy Grattage – but not in an aggressive or intimidating way – just to determine what might have upset him like that.

A man's got to do what a man's got to do, he kept thinking, largely in persuading himself that this really had to be the necessary next step. If he were perfectly honest though, he was struggling with now being considerably wary of Tommy – if not actually scared of him – and how Tommy might react on seeing Colin again so soon.

After an unfinished breakfast, consumed largely on the move, Colin set off in his car towards Sparrow Park. He felt inclined to subscribe to a principle once widely attributed to NSPCC staff, of not driving to home visits above third-gear, thereby helping to maintain a measured approach to the prospect of engaging in difficult situations.

Along the way, he tried to envisage a range of likely reactions from Tommy and particularly how he might manage any one of them. While care and concern had to be the order of the day, Colin could not confidently rule out having to defend himself. Well, so be it. If he goes for me, I shall have to be ready for that eventuality too, he thought, as he drew up just round the corner from the cul-de-sac where the family lived. He slowly, and pensively, applied his handbrake.

This was not the sort of occasion, Colin decided, for the casually familiar back-door approach. This quest was somewhat different. It could also call for a clear line of retreat. All too soon though, he found himself at the front door, where he consciously braced himself. Having taken a long deep breath, he knocked on the cracked, frosted pane. No sooner had he done so, he had second thoughts about this really being a good idea. He felt distinctly uneasy.

Too late. Tommy's silhouette could be seen approaching down the hallway. Colin drew himself up to his full height, albeit only a little more than that of Tommy. With only the closed door separating them, Tommy apparently stopped, dead still. He stood there, silent and motionless for what seemed like several moments, before slowly turning round, then ambling back towards the living room, where he firmly shut the door.

Colin remained there for several seconds, just to see if there might be any further reaction from indoors. There was none. Having largely achieved his main objective, he returned to his car to make his way ponderously back to the office. Colin was fairly sure that Tommy had realised who the caller was, and he was somewhat reassured that he had not been inclined towards any further negative reaction. He also felt at least in a slightly more confident position to discuss it all with Cora.

On returning to the office, still consumed in thought, Pam and Karen promptly jogged him back into the real world with their familiar cheery greetings. "Where've you been hiding, then?" Karen chirped.

"We thought you must have emigrated!" added Pam.

"Oh, I've just been preening myself for you pair," he quipped. "It takes some doing, I can tell you. Is Cora in?"

"Should be," replied Karen, still chirpily, and indeed to Colin's considerable relief.

He really need not have asked. Cigarette smoke was drifting blithely into the corridor from Cora's open door. More than an indication that she was in, it was rather that she was available for any queries from staff. She greeted Colin warmly, readily beckoning him inside, stubbing out a cigarette.

"Okay then, what's the latest news on Eileen Agnew?" she asked eagerly. "I hear she's been making quite a spectacle of herself in more ways than one."

"Not half," said Colin, "but Scotch Corner staff have Eileen firmly in their sights. I have sorted her benefit payments and Scotch Corner will let me know if there is anything else I may need to do. The last thing that Eileen craves is social work support. She will freely generate her own crisis for this department – whether it be me or indeed anyone else – to faithfully pick up the pieces, as and when."

"That's fair enough," Cora sighed. "It'll do for now I suppose."

"It will have to, Cora," Colin added with a hint of emphasis. He then proceeded to bring his supervisor up to date on the Grattage saga of the preceding twenty-four hours.

"Hmm…" Cora observed, lighting another cigarette and blowing out the match. "Interesting." It occurred to Colin how cigarettes could well be a source of Cora's impelling inspiration when called upon to think things through. "We'll pick this up in the supervision we've scheduled later, while planning for your forthcoming departure with bucket and spade on the handicapped holiday. Before that though," she added, "I'll see you and Maggie after lunch for a proper debrief. I'll let her know. Is that okay?"

"That's fine," said Colin, somewhat reassured, pushing himself briskly from the chair. His pigeon-hole was indicating that he had much to do.

And then, of all things, as he stepped out of Cora's office, if he didn't go and bump into Elizabeth Winstanley again!

Since Colin was now in a slightly more confident mood in the wake of current events, he was not quite so taken aback at seeing her as he had been on past occasions. "Oh, hello there, Elizabeth," he said cheerily. As she warmly returned his greeting, Colin added, "We'll have to stop meeting like this, in corridors," before immediately turning cold at realising how this clumsy, casual remark had considerable potential to be misinterpreted.

Too late, again! "Oh yes, where shall we meet then, somewhere more interesting?" Elizabeth said smilingly, and with a more than telling hint of insinuation.

"Oh, I'm sure we can think of somewhere," Colin blurted out as he made good his escape, and before the added impact of yet another trite remark made him feel even more embarrassed. Damn it! Why, oh why, he thought, as he scurried downstairs, does Elizabeth always seem to have such a destabilising effect on me like this?

He thankfully found only Annie and Glenda in the relative sanctuary of the Intake team room. They were obviously absorbed in staffing the duty shift that morning. This gave Colin a much welcome opportunity to spend time on variously returning phone calls and in almost catching up with some case recording. It also occurred to him that he might book his car in for a well-overdue service, if this could usefully coincide with his next office-based duty shift, before the advent of the handicapped holiday.

The silence was only broken upon Annie returning to the team room following a brief absence. "Well, would you believe it?" she said. "I've only just realised on going to the loo that I've come to work this morning with my knickers on inside-out." Glenda and Colin each looked up, somewhat bemused. No one said anything. That was probably as well. The three of them each got down to immersing themselves silently in what they were already doing.

The debrief with Maggie and Cora was relatively straightforward. Colin, for his part, thought how collected and unfazed Maggie had come across throughout an undeniably unnerving experience. Maggie congratulated

Colin on having the moral fibre to return to the property alone again that morning. "Having the wherewithal to speak constructively to an angry man," she observed, "about such sensitive issues as the care of his children, is a real measure of professional maturity in social work."

But Cora, however, was otherwise not quite so sure that Colin's return trip was necessarily a wise move. "You may have been somewhat fortunate that it didn't literally go belly-up for you, Colin," she said with a measure of concern. "It really needed to be discussed here in agreeing a collective way forward, one that the department could take corporate responsibility for." She then smiled and added, "But I do hand it to you unreservedly, Colin, for not shirking from doing what you felt was right."

Cora's beaming grin remained fixed as she reached for her cigarettes. "Do you really know what had upset Tommy Grattage?" she smirked, as she lit-up again.

"No, what?" murmured Colin, clearly bemused.

"It wasn't you – or Maggie, for that matter. I suspect you happened to have been convenient targets of officialdom," she announced, exhaling more plumes of smoke.

"How do you mean?" Colin asked with a furrowed brow. Maggie was similarly transfixed.

"Tommy Grattage has been arrested this morning," Cora revealed, "not long after you left, Colin. He was taken straight to court." A passing moment had Colin almost open-mouthed. Cora paused before continuing. "You may not be surprised to hear that he's in breach of a suspended sentence again that will see him on his way to prison before the day is out. Peggy Forrester, from Probation, rang to let me know. Tommy would have been aware of this looming yesterday, before you gallantly showed up to present yourselves as easy targets."

"Right then," said Colin, energetically emerging from the shock. "I'd better get round to see how June and the kids are coping with all of this."

"I think not," Cora replied. "We'll take advantage of this natural break to give Annie Wrigley the opportunity of introducing Maggie."

"What?" uttered Colin, still shocked. "Are you taking me off the case then, Cora?"

"Not at all," she confidently replied, leaning back in her chair. "But we do have to plan for your not being around with the handicapped holiday coming up soon. There seems little point in your beginning this crucial next phase, so to speak, only then for you to promptly disappear before Maggie's role gets properly under way. In any case, Colin, there are other important loose ends for you to tie up, like Sarah McNally for instance."

"Yes, I see. Good point," Colin acknowledged. Cora was clearly more aware of the bigger picture than he. "June and the kids will really be in need of support though right now," he felt obliged to add.

"Roger," replied Cora, harking back colourfully to her days as a commissioned officer in the army welfare service. "You have a chat with Annie. We'll then slot her into your next supervision session to agree the wherewithal for her covering your imminent absence.

"Fine," agreed Colin, "but for goodness sake, don't ask Annie about her knickers."

"I beg your pardon?" Cora exclaimed.

"It's okay, Cora, nothing to be alarmed about. Just an Intake in-joke," he said flippantly as he slipped out of the door. "See you later."

His task of catching up with Sarah McNally's circumstances needed to coincide with her father, Kevin, being home from work. This meant that Colin calling there on his way home seemed to make sense. Mustn't be late tonight though 'cos of being on emergency duty this evening – not to mention supervision with Cora, he thought. In the meantime, he had time to call on Doris Betts before his forthcoming absence.

Calling on Doris proved to be a familiar tonic, with rich, milky coffee and digestive biscuits into the bargain. There was very little that she required of him, beyond having him cast his eyes over various bits of correspondence and for him to advise her accordingly. Her new neighbour, Natalie, was evidently in almost daily contact and that appeared to be working out quite well. If he were patently honest, though, Doris's continuing need as someone regarded as 'socially isolated' was possibly becoming increasingly difficult to justify.

Colin eventually explained about his forthcoming absence on the handicapped holiday to Skegness. "That'll be a nice change for you," Doris quipped. Colin was by no means so sure. He had yet to find out for himself.

"Would that be something that you might enjoy, Doris?" Colin asked." A change of scenery, perhaps?" Since it had only now occurred to him, he somewhat self-consciously wondered why he had not raised this with

Doris before. He must have been distracted by the merits of milky coffee. In the event, however, he need not have worried on that score.

"You must be joking," she retorted emphatically. "What with all those decrepit old people? No thank you."

"Okay," Colin remarked with a smile, "I think I'm beginning to get your drift." He might not have expected anything less from Doris Betts. The two of them then proceeded to chat happily, about this and that, for several minutes before Colin, all too soon, needed to make his excuses to get on with other things. "I'll see you within the next four weeks then, Doris," he said, as she followed him laboriously on her sticks to the front door to wave him off.

In no time at all, following a couple of other minor jobs along the way, Colin was back at the office for supervision. It was a largely run-of-the-mill affair, with Cora deliberating over particular cases, encouraging him to summarise certain methodology and identifying plans for future action in others. More important, in some respects for Cora, was to find other ways to relieve Colin of a somewhat accumulating workload.

She then returned briefly to the skills and experience required in speaking constructively to an angry man, or woman for that matter – in understanding the emotional implications of the task, and recognising that people cannot actually be told how to 'feel' and of acknowledging their point of view, even if you don't agree with it. Beyond all that though, crucially, is having the wherewithal of encouraging them to explore options they may well have to influence – and hence deal with – the cause of their anger.

This supervision session, however, was less than routine in two other respects. Significant attention was given to identifying, along with Annie Wrigley, the ways and means how she might 'deputise' for Colin with the Grattage family in the coming weeks.

Annie's overseeing Maggie Rushton's introduction to family members provided a timely complementary focus that did not necessarily impinge directly upon anything Colin had been doing. Arrangements were duly made for Annie to make immediate contact and to liaise accordingly with Maggie. Cora felt that Colin's taking a back seat for a while was necessary in not confusing any of those crucial next steps.

The one remaining aspect of the supervision session was one that came quite out of the blue for Colin. Cora announced that she was putting his name forward for forthcoming approved social worker training. This really was something new, in more ways than one. Any notion of what was being 'approved' here referred to the capacity of social workers to carry out certain important statutory responsibilities. These were contained in forthcoming changes to mental health practice, or rather, to the legislation underpinning it.

The Mental Health Act 1983 represented the first major update of mental health legislation in twenty-five years. Approved social workers would be those professionally qualified staff specially trained in mental health work. The actual notion of 'approval' here referred to social workers being explicitly approved by their employing local authority to undertake the necessary interventions of the legislation. This extended to applying for a person with significant mental health problems to be admitted to hospital for limited periods of time, for assessment or indeed for treatment, in conjunction with the input of responsible medical staff.

At this stage in his career, Colin had not acquired the necessary training nor experience for that sort of work. His early baptism to date in the field of mental health had been confined to accompanying more experienced colleagues in a 'shadowing' capacity, often referred to as a 'sitting by Nellie' approach. This was an acknowledged means of acquainting staff with the essence of social work practice, required on behalf of people struggling with the implications of managing their mental health.

The advent of this new legislation, however, clearly expected more than that in a critical aspect of professional expertise that had considerable implications for people's civil liberties. While 'sitting by Nellie' certainly played its part in all of that, legislation and training was now demanding much more. The fact that Cora was putting Colin forward for this training seemed to indicate at least an encouraging vote of confidence from his senior social worker.

It almost banished any lingering notion he might have had about being seen as not quite up to the mark on the Grattage front. That was not to say, however, that Colin no longer harboured any self-doubt about his own ability, and that fact might perhaps have even been one of his emerging strengths.

He had to be home promptly to take up his place on the

emergency duty rota that evening. He had hardly realised just how hungry he was in the wake of another busy day. Having not long finished a hurried ready-meal, while glancing through the evening paper, he heard the telephone ring. Here we go, he thought, stand by your beds.

Sure enough, it was Barbara Durose, the duty senior. "Had your tea yet, Colin?" she asked breezily. "Got one from your patch here, if you're ready."

"Go on," he replied in a much less breezy tone, dreading a tale of woe surrounding one of his current cases.

He almost uttered an audible sigh of relief upon Barbara announcing, "This one's not apparently known to us. We've had a call from a Longley GP, Dr Duffy, concerning an old chap, Jim Spooner, aged eighty-one, who lives down in Goldenvale with his wife. Dr Duffy has been called out to Mr Spooner today following his recent discharge from hospital following a mild stroke. District nursing services are involved but he fears that the Spooners may not be coping very well. They may be in need of more support, possibly day care or even short-stay 'part-three' accommodation." Barbara was referring here to part three of the National Assistance Act 1948. Local authorities were thereby required to provide residential accommodation for elderly or infirm people, or indeed anyone in need of care and attention that was not otherwise available to them.

"And is this an emergency referral?" Colin asked glibly, highlighting a common debate about maintaining necessary priorities for an emergency service staffed by just three on-call social workers.

"Well, he is eighty-one," Barbara added, "and they are socially isolated down there in Goldenvale, with no family close by." This gave Colin the impression that it was Barbara, rather than Dr Duffy, who was trying to emphasise the emergency element here. He wondered if this senior social worker, with whom he had not previously had any contact, may have been somewhat loathe to press someone as important as a GP on the matter of elderly care priorities. The suitability of 'part three' accommodation for people struggling with evident "medical needs" was also a potential bone of contention with social workers.

Residential care under 'part three', local authorities would argue, by definition implied needs that elderly or infirm people would have for 'care and attention' rather than for any 'medical or nursing' intervention. This distinction was at the core of a debate that prevailed for years. In individual cases, of course, any compelling matter of need could only be determined upon assessment, by actually seeing the person concerned. Colin was familiar with all of that. While he wondered why Barbara had not merely agreed to pass on the GP's concerns for Longley Intake team to pursue, he was not inclined to press her further.

"Okay," said Colin. "I'm on my way." It hadn't escaped him that the job was perhaps as broad as it was long anyway. *I could well be saving myself, or even one of my colleagues, a trip out to see Mr Spooner tomorrow*, so he thought.

While Goldenvale was on the outskirts of Longley, it was an isolated community, somehow detached from the busy town centre. As its name implied, it nestled in a broad river valley that was accessed via a winding minor road, en route to a major junction of the M6. The valley had originally flourished with substantial industrial activity in post-Victorian times, when it enjoyed considerable prosperity. Much of that, however, had long since fallen into decay, leaving only a handful of small engineering firms still in business. Few people lived there now and there was no obvious community identity shared by those who did.

Colin soon found the address where the Spooners lived. It was one of a pair of fairly large Edwardian semis that gave strong impressions of having seen better times. Colin's knock at the door was soon answered by a well-presented, sprightly looking Mrs Spooner, who said meekly that she had not been expecting anyone to call. Colin introduced himself and explained the purpose of his visit, whereupon he was promptly invited in. While he always had his identity card with him, at the ready if need be, he had yet to visit anyone asking to see it before inviting him into their home and proceeding to freely divulge extensive personal histories, without a second thought.

He admired, in passing, the modest grandeur of the high ceilings of the property and the comfortable home conditions, as he was shown into the rear living room. There he saw an elderly gentleman sitting quietly, who was evidently the Mr Spooner he had come to see. A commode occupied a rather disproportionate pride of place beside the fire surround, somehow advertising the elderly gentleman's currently ailing circumstances.

"Good evening, Mr Spooner," Colin said enthusiastically. "How are you feeling?" The elderly gentleman smiled without saying anything. "Your doctor's asked me to come and see you to see if we might be able to offer you some extra support. What would you think about that?" There was still no answer and Colin thought that this could well be symptomatic of his recent stroke.

He could see no point in putting Mr Spooner through his paces, so to speak, to establish just how incapacitated he might be. There was a confirmed debilitating medical diagnosis. The matter arising here was rather about an elderly couple coping generally with the effects of that diagnosis, and, in particular, about identifying the coping mechanisms upon which they could rely.

So Colin then turned his attention to Mrs Spooner. "How are you managing with all of this?" he asked sympathetically.

"Oh, I'm all right," she said. While Colin was not particularly surprised to hear this, it did cause him to ask himself – yet again – how this matter had managed to be contrived as an emergency priority. "The nurses are visiting daily," she added. "They have also brought this commode and my niece's husband has brought the bed downstairs." Mrs Spooner showed Colin through to the front room.

This large reception room, commonly known as the parlour, was now almost exclusively occupied by a very large double bed with a highly polished walnut headboard. "Do you have any other family?" Colin asked in a low-key conversational way.

"My sister lives in Bloxwich," she replied, "and I have a niece in Cannock. They have both been very good since Jim was taken ill," she added.

"Do you have anyone more local?" Colin queried, slightly more searchingly.

"No, not really," came the reply. "We've always kept to ourselves really. We both worked well beyond retirement age."

"What did you do?" Colin asked with a smile, indicative of genuine interest.

"Jim was a toolmaker for years. I worked for Lotus," Mrs Spooner said with a degree of pride.

"Cars?" asked Colin, with a knowing smile.

"No-o, shoes, you daft thing," she said emphatically, but appreciating his quip, as they returned to Mr Spooner in the living room.

Trying a new tack, Colin put forward the idea of how some immediate outside support might help them both to cope a little better with the onset of Mr Spooner's current difficulties. While any notion of heavy-end support, like 'part three' accommodation, was unlikely to be a favourable current option, other forms of help could be of benefit. "This could even include the means of allowing Mrs Spooner the opportunity to do some shopping or even visit a friend," Colin suggested enthusiastically to the two of them. The distinctly unimpressed look on Mrs Spooner's face otherwise said it all.

But before she was able to decline the offer politely, her husband interceded. "She's been the world to me, she has," he announced suddenly and loudly, quite out of the blue.

"I don't know where I would have been without her," he added. "She's looked after me like an angel. She really has." Then he stopped, returning to his expressionless gaze.

Colin was impressed, but before he could make any sort of fitting comment, Mrs Spooner similarly interjected. "Well I promised to, didn't I, all those years ago?" Now this implicit reference here to wedding vows – and moreover to the sincerity of Mrs Spooner's evident commitment to them – evocatively spoke volumes. It now really did have Colin struggling for words. As Colin went to wipe his eyes, Mrs Spooner swiftly put her arm around her husband, hugging him tightly. This merely served to make Colin's incapacity for words even more acute.

As he blew his nose, it brought to mind a not infrequent saying of Doris Betts in suggesting how 'old age is certainly not for cowards'. Colin then began to find ways to draw this visit to a close. He said that while he fully respected the couple's wishes to decline any immediate offers of help, he would be letting his colleagues at Longley know of their current circumstances, at least for future reference.

He also left the office contact details, should the Spooners wish to get in touch. Having couched this in an optimistic sort of way, he privately suspected that neither the Spooners nor his social work colleagues would readily be in contact with one another, short of a further crisis.

Colin dutifully reported this outcome – albeit without any accompanying heart-wringing sentiments – to Barbara Durose. She thanked him accordingly for his contribution to what otherwise turned out to be a very quiet duty evening.

TEN

No fault of their own

COLIN DROPPED HIS CAR off early at Fenport service station for its well-overdue service. Having scheduled himself a car-free day as he prepared for his fast-approaching distractions in Skegness, he caught the bus from Fenport for the straightforward run into Longley. Then it was not far from the terminus to the local day centre, for what Jim Rathbone would undoubtedly be regarding as his long-awaited briefing.

The double-decker was not unusually crowded for that time in the morning, so Colin made straight for the upper deck. He found it relatively quiet up there, given the number of people on board. Further along the route, just as the bus was about to draw away from a stop on the outskirts of town, Colin saw Doris's neighbour, Natalie, appearing at the top of the stairs. She was ushering her two children in front of her to take a seat a couple of rows in front of Colin, without her noticing him.

The elder child, her son, seemed rather disgruntled, which may have partly explained the need for his mother's ushering. Since there was only one vacant seat, Natalie was obliged to lift her daughter onto her knee. She then squeezed in her son, to remain standing close beside her. This only served to deepen the boy's sullen mood. They were very likely, Colin thought, on their way to school.

It also became apparent that Natalie too was – perhaps understandably – rather flustered. She was evidently in the throes of ill-tempered exchanges with the lad that eventually led to Natalie looking him full in the face and saying sternly to him, "Now look, if you don't behave yourself, I shall tell your dad, and then you'll know about it!"

Her son, however, was neither intimidated by, nor impressed with, this veiled threat. He only announced rather loudly by way of reply, and with bristling resentment, "Yes, you do – an' I'll tell dad you've peed in our new red bucket!"

This caused Natalie to spring abruptly from her seat. She quickly rang the overhead bell before leading her kids back again – her son again by his upper arm – towards the downstairs exit, to alight at the next stop. It did seem to Colin, though, to be some distance away from the school he thought the children attended. It really looked, to all the world, like Natalie's unfettered retreat was from the widespread gazes of those on the upper deck.

Colin couldn't quite see her facial expression. This was one of those real gems, he thought to himself, that can be so eloquently spilled from the mouths of babes and sucklings. It caused him to smile all the way to the terminus.

The Pelham was one of two of the local authority's larger day centres, essentially serving the southern half of the conurbation. Its care provision catered for a wide range of elderly people and those considered handicapped. While actually being a registered handicapped person – that is someone registered as 'disabled' under The Chronically Sick & Disabled Persons Act 1970 – was not necessarily an explicit criterion for attending the centre, Pelham's longstanding traditions had been closely associated with the adjacent Workshops for the Blind.

This meant that an emphasis on engaging in handicrafts remained strong among other opportunities that the centre had to offer. It was an emphasis that largely prevailed, despite a wider, generic appreciation of 'need' beginning to find favour with contemporary thinking. Like many things, they had simply always done it that way – always handicrafts. This sort of habitual inclination would later be fittingly encapsulated by the footballer Joey Barton, of all people, in observing how people can easily become enslaved by the assumptions they grew up with.

The day centre manager, Jim, who actually went by the title of Officer-in-Charge, was indeed a relic of the bygone Workshops era. He therefore prided himself on the handicrafts approach to services offered, and curried favour unreservedly with those clients who were inclined to immerse themselves in such activities. He was, by contrast, less disposed towards those who merely wished to sit and chat and read the paper, or even to just play cards with one another for goodness sake!

No sooner had Colin set foot inside Pelham on arrival than he found himself warmly greeted by Mr Rathbone, who exuberantly shook his hand. It caused Colin to wonder whether he might have actually been lying in wait for him. Jim beckoned Colin enthusiastically to follow him through to his office, where he proudly held open the door for his visitor. The expansive office was liberally festooned with framed photographs. Most of them explicitly featured Jim – often with a rather exaggerated, camera-conscious smile – and actively joining in the centre's activities. Other photographs, arguably in more prominent positions, were of formal occasions held at the centre with any number of civic dignitaries.

Jim actually rubbed his hands with glee upon getting down to the real business of explaining about the holiday to Skegness, that he clearly regarded as yet another jewel in Pelham's crown. Thereafter, Jim simply went into monologue, occasionally pursing his lips to exaggerate the pronunciation of certain words. His pencil-thin, shaved moustache somehow served to enhance the diction of these exaggerations. He spoke continuously and without appearing to draw breath. While his overview was unfaltering, it was not necessarily eloquent. Despite that, Colin was able to glean elements of useful information about an undertaking of which he really had little prior conception, beyond its somewhat cynical reputation among the wider workforce. The prospect overwhelmingly occurred to him that the ways and means of transporting large numbers of disabled people halfway across the country, some with escorts, and considerable disability equipment, should not be underestimated.

He learned that the holiday was centred upon the Miners' Welfare holiday camp in Skegness, very much in the guise of typical holiday camps that became popular from the 1950s. Jim explained how Colin would be expected to assume social work responsibility for the people on his particular coach, rather like a sort of social work holiday rep. The exact nature of those responsibilities otherwise remained vague. Just getting on with it seemed to be the general expectation. Any understanding of what might actually be required seemed to be taken as read, since Jim didn't broach with Colin in any way, what Colin's experience in this aspect of social work might have been. He didn't even ask if Colin had any questions.

That apart, Jim did explain that another more senior and experienced social worker, one Richard Ingram, would have overall responsibility during the holiday. While that name meant nothing to Colin, it appeared to represent a gratifying element of Jim's soliloquy. Entertainment, he gathered, would be provided by the camp's resident staff. Additional assistance to the holidaymakers would also be provided by a team of local police cadets. This laudable initiative had reciprocal merits of providing aspiring police officers with insight and experience in relating to the needs of disabled people, and indeed to the wider public.

Then Jim rubbed his hands again and smiled. With a rather sly nudge-nudge wink-wink sort of grin, Jim added, still rubbing his hands, "And there'll be some nice young policewomen on this trip too." Colin, however, didn't quite know what to say, nor indeed what Jim expected. His reaction was merely limited to a limply smiling acknowledgement, lost for words.

The briefing then meandered towards its natural conclusion. Jim shook Colin's hand again and said how he was looking forward to seeing him on Monday morning for the grand lift-off. Colin acknowledged this by saying how much he was looking forward to it too. This was probably something that Jim was expecting to hear, rather than Colin's telling reaction to his overview. He had by then concluded that pressing Jim for further details would be less than worthwhile.

On his return to the office, Colin felt obliged to attend to a string of neglected administrative jobs, including case recording, of course, prior to his imminent absence. There was a strange feeling attached to this of somehow being legitimately excused from what he would regard as normal duties in favour of less demanding, routine chores.

Ivor Axford entered the team room with an unusually cheery air, greeting Colin with an enthusiastic, "Hiya, Teach," without averting his gaze from a letter in his hand. "Gather you're off on the handicapped jollies sometime soon?"

On this occasion, however, it sounded not quite so insincere. It was rather in the tone of more friendly banter for Ivor. His addressing Colin commonly enough as 'Teach' remained something he could never be entirely sure about. Either way, it was of little matter. Ivor was very much one on his own anyway. He would sometimes regale colleagues with tales of past experiences in army service. These gave strong indications of a much-savoured period in Ivor's life, often tempered with bawdy innuendo that Colin suspected was intentionally paraded for the benefit of his mixed audience in the Intake team.

Then Colin's phone rang. He picked it up with a cheery greeting, expecting to hear Pam or Karen at the other end. It was, to his surprise, Elizabeth Winstanley no less. This caught him slightly off guard. "Wondered if I could pick your brains," she pondered meekly.

"Sure," said Colin, wondering for the life of him what pearls of wisdom he could possibly impart to Elizabeth.

"If you're going to be in for a little while," she said, "it might be better if I popped down to explain."

"By all means," Colin replied, intrigued. "I'll put the kettle on."

Elizabeth arrived in the Intake team room in no time at all. She explained, as Colin made the coffee, how she had just taken the case of a juvenile offender, named Ellis Bott, who had previously been well known to Colin. The young man in question had subsequently been committed to care by the court and placed in a community home, St Vincent's, situated near the Welsh border. Having only just taken responsibility for the case, not to mention the implications of distance, Elizabeth had not yet had any opportunity of meeting the young man.

"And I now discover that he has a review coming up in barely three weeks' time," she added in exasperation.

"While I will certainly get out to see him next week, as well as needing to introduce myself to his family of course, I would very much appreciate having someone accompany me to the review who has a better grip of background knowledge. It's the very least that Ellis deserves," she added dolefully.

"How can I refuse that sort of plea?" Colin replied. "I'll have to check it out with Cora but I'm sure she won't mind. She has a passion for young offenders. Since I'm in Skegness next week though, I'll have little opportunity to fill you in before the review," he explained, before immediately being struck by yet another inappropriate turn of phrase to this particularly attractive colleague.

"You can fill me in en route to the review then," Elizabeth returned in an instant, and with a plainly knowing smile that caused Colin to blush. He hurriedly busied himself by making a careful note, head down, of the forthcoming review date in his diary.

Once Elizabeth returned to her office, Colin got back to his list of other jobs. High among those priorities was that of conferring with Mrs Healey, at Eversleigh Nursery School, about Sarah McNally's recent progress. Catching up later with Sarah's father was to be one of his final throws of the dice that week.

"All seems well," Mrs Healey announced optimistically. "She is still of course one of our more limited children, who will probably require additional support in school. In other respects though, she is doing okay. Her attendance is good, though mum often brings her in late. I think we are quite confident now that Sarah's distress was attributed to the dog being run-over. We happen to have heard about it from any number of different sources.

"On that point though," Mrs Healey added, "I would like to apologise for the false alarm and for any unnecessary work it may have caused."

"No apologies necessary," Colin replied confidently, finding himself beginning to warm towards this headteacher. "There are too many reminders these days of potentially negative consequences to professional indifference to a child's distress," he added, inwardly cringing again at the prospect of Sarah's father being arrested at work following the death of his dog.

Ringing off from Mrs Healey, Colin brought Sarah's mum to mind and how his initial impressions of her had somehow reminded him of June Grattage. He wondered again about the extent to which the number of children some parents have directly influences their potential for child-rearing. Of the Grattage children for instance, only Dawn, the eldest, could perhaps be seen to continue to make anything like satisfactory progress. While her overall potential was inevitably limited by the nature of family circumstances, she had probably benefited from being the eldest child whose formative years would have been less compromised by the competing demands of other siblings.

That reinforced for Colin how support to families makes such a positive difference – whether it comes from a supportive partner, from wider family or indeed from outside the family circle. Perhaps Sarah's mum would also benefit from input from the likes of Maggie Rushton, he thought. *There again, though, wouldn't we all?* he postulated.

Towards the end of the afternoon, Colin made his way to catch the bus back to Fenport to collect his car. "Bring us a stick of rock back!" shouted Karen as he signed out of the office.

"Well, you lot down here will more than likely be among the cheeky postcard brigade. That's if I have any time to give folk round here a second thought next week," he said, glancing over his shoulder. "If I survive, that is," he added, before bidding a final "Cheerio."

On the short bus journey, Colin's mind drifted immediately back to poor Natalie and her public embarrassment that morning. He wondered if she had yet recovered from it, not to mention whether there had been any unseemly repercussions. Having collected his car, he then had to retrace much of that journey to make his way to see Sarah McNally's father, Kevin Hollins. En route he began to have second thoughts about the wisdom of calling unannounced, and at around tea time. He had originally favoured catching Kevin off guard, or at least unrehearsed, in trying to gauge a realistic impression of family life and in particular how or whether recent events might have adversely affected Sarah.

Now, however, he was not so sure. Nor indeed was he sure whether social services had any legitimate role in this family's circumstances whatsoever. He eventually persuaded himself that he was just tying up loose ends, largely by way of courtesy to the little girl's dad, in taking his perspective into account.

When Kevin Hollins, however, answered his door – still dressed in what looked like his working clothes – to find a social worker on the doorstep, courtesies proved not to be particularly high on the agenda. "What the hell do you want?" he growled when Colin politely introduced himself.

Colin tamely went for a half-truth: "Sarah's school have been just a little concerned that she has not been herself of late, sometimes unduly upset in the classroom. We just wondered whether this was something you might have noticed."

"And what the hell's that got to do with social services?" retorted Hollins. "Do you want her in care then? Well, it will damned well be over my dead body, and probably yours as well, while we're at it." Kevin Hollins was livid.

"Not at all," said Colin, trying hard to maintain composure. "We simply just want to include you in any consideration given to finding the most appropriate way to support Sarah in school." Cora's recent reference to professional maturity being demonstrated by talking to an angry man, particularly about the welfare of his children, came flooding again into Colin's mind.

"And why can't the school talk to me about that?" Hollins asked, perhaps not unreasonably, apart from the searing tone of his voice.

"It's just difficult for them to contact you, I suppose, with your being at work throughout the week," Colin observed in a softer tone. He then followed this by clinging again to another half-truth by saying, "We've just been doing some work in school recently and I offered to call on you to get your point of view."

"You should talk to her mother then, shouldn't you?" Hollins retorted with unabated anger.

"School are doing just that," Colin assured him, "but this is merely taking your point of view into account as well. You're Sarah's dad, and dads are unique."

At this, Hollins's demeanour appeared to soften. "You'd better come in then, mate," he said as he stepped aside, fully opening the door. "Do you want a cup o' tea?" Colin gladly accepted this familiar peace offering, in spite of his not really liking tea at all. In doing so, it had not escaped him how this could well be regarded as further dishonesty on his part. It filled him with little satisfaction.

Kevin soon emerged from the kitchen with a mug of tea clasped in each hand. He handed one to Colin, who found that the mugs must have each been rinsed in cold water, without being dried, before having hot water poured onto the tea bags. As Colin took a couple of sips to acclimatise himself to the taste, Kevin was first to speak. "Sarah was really upset," he announced, "when the dog got run over. He'd been around since before she was born. It was upsetting for all of us," he added with a hint of sadness.

"Yes, I heard about that," Colin said sympathetically, and now much more comfortable in honest exchanges. "How's she been since?"

"Well, okay really," he replied. "She talks about Dickie a lot – well we both do – 'cos he was really part of the family and…" Kevin faltered for a brief moment before continuing, "but I think kids sometimes have a simpler way of looking at life and death than grown-ups. They see that people live and then they die and everybody just has to get on with it," he said with a confident element of feeling.

While Colin was not quite so sure on that point, he respected Hollins's view, and their discussion moved into a more free-flowing, two-way conversation – mainly about Sarah of course, who her dad saw for some time most weekends, but with Kevin feeling that there was no way back for him and Sarah's mum. Nothing was revealed in that discussion to cause Colin any real concern on Sarah's behalf. While it did not extend to anything like an assessment of a child to whom Colin had not really spoken, the picture was emerging that further probing might not be necessary.

Colin eventually offered Kevin Hollins his outstretched hand prior to making his departure. Kevin's response was limp, not at all enthusiastic. "Should you ever have the need to get in touch about Sarah, feel free to give us a call," Colin said, handing him his visiting card as he left. There was no reply.

Returning to his car, Colin reflected upon the turn of events surrounding the Dickie episode. While he was inclined to regard the false alarm triggered by those two words as entirely genuine, he was less than sure whether Kevin Hollins might have somehow just put one over on him.

What actually troubled Colin more was his own blatant inability to have been honest with Hollins throughout. Then again, he would have struggled to find any coherent form of words to satisfactorily explain the basis of the head teacher's original concern. "Talk about the truth hurting," he kept saying to himself, all through the evening.

He was still unsure as the night wore on. On several occasions through an unusually long night, Colin found himself having to get out of bed to go to the toilet. Ruminating over a severe bout of acute diarrhoea, sitting motionless on successive occasions, barely awake, he kept asking himself whether Hollins was indeed having the last word. Surely any connection between the purpose of his earlier visit to Sarah's father, the tea he drank there and this nocturnal aftermath was purely coincidental.

Or was it? It was likely that he would never get to know.

ELEVEN

Handicapped Holidays

IT WAS CONSIDERABLY MORE than welcome relief for Colin to find he had the benefit of a whole weekend to recover from the Hollins visit. For much of that time, his mind continually flitted between wondering if Kevin Hollins may have somehow discovered the truth behind his and Annie's visit to his daughter in school before putting that remote possibility quite out of his mind.

Realising on one hand that such a quandary would get him nowhere, he couldn't find much else to do. He was not inclined in any way to stray far from the bathroom. His mind would occasionally turn to the prospects of what Skegness might hold and then, almost surprisingly, to the thought of not seeing Elizabeth again for some time. While he did not think that she was married, he did have cause to wonder if she could be cosily entwined in some other sort of emotional commitment, or then perhaps not. *Hmm… she does seem to warm towards me a bit though*, he thought.

Then, in no time, Colin was woken by bright sunlight streaming through his bedroom curtains. It was D-Day for Skegness! Being intent upon an early start, and indeed he was, any further expectations he might have had about being among the first on parade were quickly dashed.

Turning into the minor road leading to Pelham day centre, he could hardly believe his eyes. Three enormous luxury coaches, filling nearly the whole street, were being loaded with luggage and larger items of disability equipment. Any number of people seemed to be scurrying in all directions. Having parked his car behind the day centre, Colin went in search of Jim. He was, of course, immediately identifiable, not only from his size and his smart suit, but by waving his long arms and issuing orders about what had to go where. There was clearly a precise place for everything and everybody as far as Jim was concerned.

He immediately beamed upon spotting Colin. "Mr Millwood!" he bellowed, striding enthusiastically towards him to shake his hand. "This is your coach," he announced proudly, beckoning Colin towards the second vehicle in the line, "Coach B." A large sticker was prominently displayed on the windscreen. Colin was promptly presented with a large manila envelope containing a detailed list of Coach B passengers and miscellaneous additional information comprising of emergency telephone contacts and the like.

"Although you will be stopping at Nottingham for a comfort break," Jim continued, again somewhat in the format of a running commentary, "you will see that there are also two red buckets stored on board each coach.

This is because handicapped people's waterworks are not very clever." Colin was immediately struck by the wide-ranging generalised versatility that society apparently attributed to red buckets and how, in the confines of his relatively sheltered upbringing, this had somehow passed him by. He struggled though, as Jim Rathbone continued unfalteringly in his commentary, to put that query into any sensibly constructed form of words. Any fleeting opportunity immediately disappeared. Beyond that though, he really did wish to ask about the ways and means of providing someone – not to mention someone who may be disabled – with the necessary dignity and privacy of relieving themselves on a crowded coach. The continuous commentary, however, harboured little time for such minor nuances.

In any case, there was plenty for Colin to do. He began introducing himself to passengers who wandered in their ones and twos towards Coach B with slips of paper in their hands. Colin made sure their luggage was placed ready for loading into the hold, before he finally ticked them off his list as they stepped aboard. Well, that was the general idea. In the event, of course, many holidaymakers could be forgiven for not knowing which particular coach might be theirs and Colin only had one list of names, just for Coach B, to which he could refer.

Many relied typically, of course, on their best instincts. Some wandered around haplessly until a member of the day centre staff eventually spotted their dilemma and pointed them in the right direction. Others strode purposefully to the nearest coach – irrespective of which one it happened to be – to secure front seats. Once there, with seat belts firmly fastened, they were all set to argue squatters' rights with anyone who cared to come along. Those requiring window seats, of course –'because my doctor says'– became too numerous to mention. Getting this show on the road, Colin thought, is going to be no mean feat.

Amid all that considerable confusion, however, he was at least able to introduce himself fleetingly to each of the other two social workers, Rhona and Chris, who had similarly been plunged, unaware, into this hive of activity. Their baptism of fire soon had them sucked into the midst of this unspoken, evolving whirlwind of a process, which only a few of its participants fully understood. For the life of him, Colin could not understand why Jim had not originally undertaken to meet all three social workers together in preparing them in a more organised way for this major undertaking. He also wondered if Rhona had been properly briefed on the on-board drill for dealing with passengers' 'waterworks' in transit.

It soon became evident that those with significant mobility problems, inevitably including wheelchair users, could hardly be denied the convenience of front seats. Even the most obstructive interloper had to be persuaded to accept that. Many did so with unedited grumbling, and sometimes only to discover their double-whammy of having to relocate well towards the rear of the coach after all. It was very apparent that their holiday would not necessarily be getting off to a good start.

After what seemed like an endless process, including that of accommodating late arrivals, the coaches were at last ready to leave. As Jim Rathbone stepped back, smilingly admiring the assembled convoy, its grand departure was suddenly forestalled by a Ford Capri screeching round the corner at speed. It stopped suddenly by Jim who bent down, evidently to exchange words briefly with the driver. The car then promptly turned sharply, again at speed, into the day centre car park. From there, a tall chap with long dark hair emerged nonchalantly carrying a holdall. Colin thought he looked like a rock star.

Jim then went to each of the coaches where he asked each of the three social workers to spare him a moment. This, it turned out, was to introduce the late arrival. He was Richard Ingram, the social worker nominated to take overall responsibility for the trip. No sooner had those introductions hurriedly been made, of course, there was no further time to lose. Mr Ingram boarded the first coach, Coach A, along with Rhona, before the coaches immediately moved slowly in line towards the main road. Their next port of call would be Nottingham.

It was a largely uneventful journey, bearing in mind that Colin remained somewhat on tenterhooks throughout, in dread of a proverbial red bucket being required. He busied himself by circulating up and down the rows of seats to make early introductions and, hopefully he thought, distracting anyone's attention from their bladder. He was struck by how considerably sociable nearly everyone appeared. He thought they seemed really nice people.

Many of the more disabled individuals had brought along a friend or relative, officially designated as an escort, to support them in getting the most from their holiday. Escorts in these circumstances would often be accommodated in the same chalet as the person they were accompanying. While some of the passengers were lone individuals, others were elderly couples. It was not necessarily clear what particular nature of disability some may have had in qualifying them, so to speak, to embark on a handicapped holiday. Colin acknowledged unquestioningly how certain disabilities and other medical conditions were not necessarily apparent to the naked eye.

The party eventually arrived at Nottingham in bright sunshine, where the coaches drew into a lay-by immediately next to public conveniences. It was obviously a well-trodden route. The driver duly announced a half-hour comfort break that conveniently took additional account of anyone, drivers included, requiring a smoke. Colin, at this point, was unsure just how proactive he was required to be in facilitating access – for people designated as 'handicapped'– in and out of the toilets. As it turned out, however, anyone requiring that sort of help was invariably assisted by an escort.

But, it was only at this late stage that Colin realised that none of the band of experienced day centre workers, who actually knew most of the people on the trip – and who had been so 'in tune' in loading the coaches for departure – appeared to be anywhere on board, unless they were travelling on other coaches. Rhona and Chris, however, soon confirmed that they were not. "They all stayed with big Jim," Rhona said facetiously, "merrily waving us off."

"You can see why it's such a popular event in the social services calendar," Chris observed. "The day centre loads all its clients onto three buses and invites eager social workers to take them away for a week. Great. Job done."

He made a point of repeating this to Richard Ingram, whose reaction was little more than a dismissive shrug of the shoulders. "We'll be all right," Richard said passively. "Make the most of it."

Meanwhile, the half-hour comfort break eventually turned into another drawn-out affair. The performance of originally getting everyone onto the coaches at the day centre was re-enacted almost in its entirety. Colin could not believe the number of people who were plainly unable to recall which coach they were on, nor indeed, having been re-directed to it, where they had actually been sitting on the first leg of the journey.

It was eventually to Colin's considerable relief to find his, and at least one other, coach at last easing their way into the holiday camp before drawing to a halt. There they were welcomed by a jovial band of resident staff in blue uniforms. To his even greater relief, the journey had been completed without even one red bucket being required. Colin was soon to discover, however, that more testing challenges had not yet begun.

It had all started well enough. Passengers identified on Colin's list were courteously shown to their chalets by the uniformed staff. They were thereafter invited to meet up afterwards in the dining hall for a reception with afternoon tea and cakes and where a brief overview of basic 'things you need to know' would take place. Nevertheless, within a very short space of time – before Colin had even found his way to the chalet he would be sharing with Chris –

a number of individuals began to present themselves in relatively quick succession with a range of concerns.

"I've been given a chalet I'm expected to share with a man!" exclaimed one extremely disgruntled woman, with good reason.

"My luggage has disappeared," lamented a tall, fit-looking man.

"I have to have four pillows," announced another clearly displeased man, "my doctor says."

"Here we go again," Colin uttered privately under his breath. GPs locally must have little else to do, he thought, beyond stipulating patients' expressed requirements upon the advent of the handicapped holiday season.

Perhaps unsurprisingly, each of these potential disasters was quickly resolved. The first woman had originally been misdirected to her chalet before being eventually relocated, male-free, to her considerable satisfaction. The lost-luggage man found his suitcase had been delivered directly to his chalet, while the man in need of more pillows was, well… simply given more pillows! It was as searching as that.

Colin at last found himself free to find Chris in negotiating their way to their own allocated chalet. They were wearily plodding, luggage-laden, up a stone stairwell to a particular first-floor landing when they met, descending at some speed, two young women who Colin recognised from one of the other Pelham coaches. They had been identified during the Nottingham stop as two policewomen. It turned out they were escorts for two of the day centre clients, who they had got to know on previous handicapped holidays when they had been police cadets. This was for them another return trip, escorting the same two women, though they did not actually share their chalet. Colin found this commitment to continuity, in their own time too, to be quite impressive.

But, before Colin or Chris had time to draw breath or utter any sort of greeting, the first young woman snapped, "Have you seen the state of the showers?"

"They're absolutely disgusting," barked the second. "What are you going to do about them?"

Colin, weary as he was, clung steadfastly to positive intent. "We'll just drop our bags off, ladies, then you can show us the grim realities of these parts of Skegness. We'll only be a couple of minutes. Where will we find you?"

"We're in chalet 124," said the first policewoman, in a now much more cordial vein. The two social workers duly dropped their luggage off, and, with little more than a glance around what appeared to be very favourable quarters, went in search of 124. "Come on in," rang out, in response to Chris's tap on the door.

Colin promptly introduced himself and Chris as they stepped inside. He went on to explain how they were two fairly 'green' social workers who had found themselves unquestionably requisitioned for this holiday bonanza.

"We have been persuaded that it is intended to boost our professional development," Chris added with a mild hint of sarcasm.

"I'm Helen," said the first young woman, "and this is Moira. We're normally policewomen by day, but this week we are posing as holiday escorts to two ladies on the trip."

"Under cover then," Colin quipped, but his witticism was lost on the others.

The four of them spent a couple of minutes in acknowledging the merits and otherwise of their immediate surroundings, until Helen and Moira suddenly realised they were cutting it fine in taking their charges to the teatime reception.

"We'll catch you there," said Colin, "following our shower-block survey."

"Perhaps you can make yourselves known to Rhona and explain what we're up to," added Chris, "and even to Richard, the chap in charge, who even we have not yet really got to know."

The two social workers were soon to discover that the showers in question, only one set of two servicing the whole of that block, were indeed pretty dismal. Police evidence was apparently spot on. Colin and Chris accordingly proceeded to make representation directly at the camp office. There it emerged that, since social workers and police officers could be properly regarded as staff, as the woman in the office explained, they could have access to more agreeable staff facilities nearby. In the meantime, of course, further attention would be given to the presentation of the standard showering facilities, bearing in mind certain inevitable limitations. "We're not exactly Sunset Strip round here, you know," the woman added with a wry smile.

The two policewomen were themselves impressed with the outcome of this episode of social work intervention. It perhaps began something of a certain upward trend, since the next twenty-four hours or more of settling in actually went quite well. There was plenty of entertainment on offer, courtesy of blue uniforms, particularly for those who enjoyed bingo and sing-along sessions – and bearing in mind that this was well before karaoke had apparently been invented. Beyond those attractions, the weather was warm and sunny, which gave plenty of opportunity for some to socialise around the swimming pool.

One particularly dramatic highlight, however, befell bathers at the poolside upon a keen-eyed police cadet diving in to retrieve a young man from the bottom of the deep end. Other cadets joined in to help revive the bather, who was not from the Pelham party, and who appeared to be 'mentally handicapped'. Thankfully to all concerned, the non-swimmer soon made a full recovery, no worse for wear, before being happily reunited, to considerable relief, with his grateful carers.

It also transpired that Colin and Chris found that they rubbed along quite well with one another. Sharing a similarly laid-back disposition, they had common incentives for engaging in social work. Chris, however, was a much more recent appointment to the profession. He was in fact a residential social worker, recently appointed to a newly opened 'state of the art' unit for children with disabilities. His posting on the handicapped holiday was intended as an opportunity to widen his appreciation of how adults compensate for challenges posed by disability. Colin though, for his part, could not quite understand the logic of that, given the myriad of influences on any child's development. It was more likely, he thought, to be yet another ploy in attracting eager new recruits into staffing these holiday excursions.

He was inclined to agree with Chris's earlier assertion that social workers on this trip could well be regarded, to some extent, as really soft options for the benefit of others. Their sharing a chalet, however, was certainly no problem. In fact it had distinct advantages in enabling the two of them to agree daily priorities, often in complementary ways. This also extended to getting to know Richard Ingram. While 'Rich' remained someone of few words, he was in fact quite sociable following first acquaintance. Colin thought he was perhaps implicitly shy.

Rich certainly rallied noticeably at any mention of football. It turned out he was a big – a really big – Bristol Rovers fan. It was therefore more than coincidence that he invested considerable energy in arranging a five-a-side soccer competition. While this was primarily among the police cadets, it was open to anyone who considered themselves fit enough to take part. Colin thought this a subtle tactic, strategically inspired to generate shared incentives away from any enduring focus on 'handicap'. That said, Rich otherwise successfully managed to avoid investing too heavily in many other aspects of the holiday experience.

The soccer competition also turned out to be something from which Helen Harrison and Moira Gillespie had no intention of being excluded. They could tackle and shoulder charge among any of the best of the male cadets. For the rest of the time, however, the two policewomen remained impressively committed to the women they were escorting. First priority throughout each day was the women's own preferences of activity. This, perhaps unsurprisingly, seldom brought them in close proximity to the swimming pool.

Beyond the teething troubles of those first few hours following their arrival, there were frankly few other early set-backs. Having said that, Colin had not appreciated until sometime afterwards, that one elderly passenger from Coach A had been taken ill en route. Moreover, she had subsequently been admitted to hospital in Nottingham. This had of course explained Richard Ingram's late arrival, and, not least, that of his not being around to field that morass of early queries.

Among other more minor difficulties, the social workers had found themselves unwittingly on steep learning curves in dealing with punctures on wheelchairs. There were also vague rumours circulating of thefts from chalets and occasional squabbles to be placated among those more impatient guests. These upsets often arose at meal times and gatherings at evening variety shows, when disputes about who was sitting where could become distinctly competitive.

It was during these evening events that Colin, usually along with Chris, would bump into the two policewomen during the course of their escorting duties. On one particular evening at a variety event, it became apparent that one of the other more disabled guests, a young woman with a severe muscle-wasting condition, had become rather inebriated while watching the show. This led to her becoming increasingly loud and argumentative with her escort, Brenda, an inoffensive and well-meaning volunteer from a charitable organisation.

Policewoman Helen could see this beginning to get out of hand, whereupon she took the initiative to intervene, tactfully but firmly, and thankfully to good effect. The young woman eventually calmed down at Helen's timely intervention. It was agreed between Helen and the escort that the young woman should return to her chalet and would perhaps benefit from an early night. Helen said that she would accompany them, leaving Bettie, the woman she was herself escorting, happily disposed with Moira for a short time.

She asked Colin if he would mind going along too, just in case. Colin was of course happy to oblige. The fractious young woman soon became far more composed. Colin thought this may have been the product of the extra attention she was evidently receiving and the debilitating effects of an unusually excessive intake of alcohol. As the four of them made their way across the camp-site, the warm summer evening appeared to have an additionally sobering, relaxing effect on each of them. Escaping the noise of a ballroom in full swing certainly had advantages in evoking a calmer, more serene influence all round.

It transpired that the young woman at the centre of this episode had a twin sister, similarly affected by the same tragic debilitating condition, and that the two of them were in fact together on this holiday, sharing a chalet with their two volunteer escorts. Upon entering the chalet, however, Colin was immediately struck by a strong pungent smell. Its source became instantly apparent, in more ways than one. A row of unwashed wet knickers was vividly on display along the top of a very warm radiator. "Leave this to me," said Helen, with a knowing nod and a briskly sweeping removal of the offending underwear. "It'll be all right now, no need to worry. You just wait outside, Colin, if you don't mind. Brenda and I will get her into bed and everything will be fine. Just hang on for me for a few minutes."

While it was inevitably more than just a few minutes, Colin did not mind at all. He admired the camp surroundings in the fading twilight, confident that this minor crisis was in capable hands. "Phew," exclaimed Helen on eventually emerging from the chalet. "Whatever did you make of that exhibition?"

"Er, were you able to, er, tackle the issue of the drying washing?" he asked delicately.

"It's all in the wash and no mistake," Helen replied emphatically. "Goodness alone knows what those two escorts are playing at!" Colin was caused to wonder how on earth he might have tackled that particular problem before concluding that it warranted no further thought. He was merely and yet again grateful for such authoritative police intervention. Then, just as the two of them were rounding a corner to return towards the illuminated glare of the ballroom, a dark figure darted at speed from one of the chalets. In a flash, and without a word, Helen immediately gave chase. Although the individual had a head-start, the two of them quickly disappeared in the direction of the unlit maze of chalets at the edge of the camp.

Upon initially being rooted, palely mesmerised to the spot, Colin dismissed any notion of joining the chase since they were already way out of reach. Well, he thought, I wouldn't wager this leading to anything like the success of the wet washing episode. The dark figure had a distinct advantage.

While Colin initially jogged tamely into the distance, looking vainly all around, he could see neither sight nor sound of anyone at all. There was no alternative, he thought, to just making his way back to the ballroom. But what, he contemplated, if Helen is now in some sort of danger? Unable to think of anything else he might do, he thought it perhaps best to confer with Moira. She would probably know what to do.

As it happened, however, Moira agreed that options were limited. "Helen will very likely have to give up the chase and make her way back," she concluded. "We will at least be able to report it. Did you get sight of the individual in terms of any sort of description?"

Colin had to admit he had not. Nor had he even been initially alert to the prospect of criminal activity. It did occur to him to let Richard Ingram know before making representation to the camp authorities, and probably in turn to the local police. All of that, however, was suddenly interrupted by a commotion in the foyer. There, in full view of gathering onlookers, Helen was maintaining a firm grip on a struggling teenager who was swearing profanely. The two of them each sported the muddied spoils of a chase along the beach. While two police cadets promptly took over from Helen in restraining the youth, another was already engaged in contacting the police. It seemed that the chalet thefts mystery could well have reached its epic climax.

Colin was impressed. While he and Moira attended swiftly to the welfare of the heroine, it surprisingly turned out she was no worse for wear. This was in spite of her energetically leaping in pursuit over what looked like a low wooden beach groyne, only to find to her horror, a six-foot drop on the other side. The offender, however, had apparently fared even worse at that obstacle and this was where it was effectively game over. It was still a hell of a long way to drag him back though, Colin thought. Goodness knows how she managed it.

More than that, it became something of yet another turning-point. It was almost inevitable, in the wake of a largely successful and enjoyable week, that Colin and Chris should ask Helen and Moira if they would care to join them at their table at the forthcoming traditional end-of-week staff party. This was an occasion that Jim Rathbone routinely attended as another golden opportunity to bask in the glamour of civic highlight. True to form, however, a happy time was certainly shared by all, and, not least, the newly acquainted quartet. It seemed like icing on the cake.

What had begun for Colin as an unanticipated, testing holiday challenge, turned into his dreading the prospect of it coming to an end. He did, however, perhaps somewhat uncharacteristically, manage to ask Helen if she and Bettie would care to join him on Coach B for the trip home. Moreover, and to his delight, she seemed really pleased to accept.

Getting the show on the road for its return trip was of course another major undertaking, and, this time, without the decisive intervention of well-rehearsed day centre staff. All of the social workers, other than Rich of course, were up early in preparing to gather equipment and to rouse bleary-eyed guests. Police cadets and staff in blue uniforms also thankfully pulled their weight to good effect. The three coaches eventually managed to snake their way slowly, in exiting camp, almost on schedule.

Colin and Helen chatted effortlessly, reflecting on many of the ups and downs of the past week. Their spontaneous, free-flowing exchanges sometimes dipped into sharing bits of information about themselves, their families and contemplating some of their ambitions. It became somehow entirely fitting in that context for Colin to ask Helen if he might be able to see her again. Although she seemed a little taken aback at this suggestion, she accepted with a broad smile. "What about tomorrow evening then?" Colin asked. "Might that be okay?"

"Oh… er… well, I think that should be okay," she replied somewhat hesitantly, before adding another broad smile.

It was not until the coaches eventually returned to Pelham that Colin's euphoria took something of a downturn. Day centre staff broke the news on arrival that the woman who had been taken ill on the outward journey, and taken to hospital in Nottingham, had sadly passed away. "It's not the first time that's happened," one of the centre supervisors observed, "where someone dies on holiday or sometimes within a couple of weeks of getting home."

In every other respect, however, a considerable number of people kindly took the time and trouble of thanking each of the social workers for helping to provide such an enjoyable trip. These unanticipated congratulations were uttered, quite fittingly as it happened, in big Jim Rathbone's earshot too. Jim glowed proudly, evidently basking in his own share of bestowed honours.

"All set for next year then, you social workers?" he proffered with a big smile. The social workers duly blushed, largely in trying to avoid any casual eye contact. They were similarly keen in avoiding any overambitious reflections of the week in the mesmerising euphoria of its evident success. With heads down, they hurried to their cars.

TWELVE

Typically Malone

THE TWENTY-FOUR HOURS OR so after dropping Helen off from the return coach at a junction near her home, and retracing much of that same route in calling to take her out on the following evening, Colin had spent in an elated daze. The Skegness undertaking, which he had been contemplating with such mixed feelings, had turned out to eclipse any previous emotion he may have ever known. While glowing feedback from a handful of very grateful holidaymakers had certainly gone some way in endorsing Colin's satisfaction, his crucially getting to know Helen had quite tipped all of that glory into the shade.

Time dragged on endlessly it seemed before he would see her again. Unable to turn his attention to anything constructive, Colin spent much of the day flitting successively between superficial tasks, without really achieving much at all. Unsurprisingly, he had showered and changed well in advance of any amount of time he actually needed to get ready.

It then followed, of course, that he found himself approaching much too early the road where Helen lived. This was in spite of adopting the now well-rehearsed NSPCC 'third gear approach'. Still too early! Parking up unobtrusively round the corner from Helen's front door, idling away yet more time, Colin reflected upon the prospect of a lady's acknowledged privilege of not having to be ready on time.

Helen opened the door. She sported her characteristically broad smile with an enthusiastic, "Hiya, come on in," as she stepped aside to let him pass. Colin drew something of a deep breath in striding courteously over the threshold. He had assumed Helen would have favoured a more prompt getaway for their first real 'date'.

"You'll have to meet my mam," she said cheerily. "I've told her all about you, and she likes to make a point of knowing just whose company I'm keeping."

"Oh, fine," Colin uttered, though wincing inwardly at the unanticipated prospect of having to present himself for a searching inspection. He need not have worried, however. Mrs Harrison merely wished to clap eyes on this anonymous stranger and perhaps just see what he looked like. In every other respect it was all very brief, with minimal nervous exchanges, before the young couple made good their getaway in a mutual whirl of excitement.

Colin had reserved a table for dinner at what he considered to be a fairly up-market venue. Helen, however, on learning of their destination, felt her stomach beginning to churn. This had less to do with first-date nerves, nor any insider information concerning a restaurant that just happened to be on her 'patch', but rather about her acute embarrassment as a self-confessed 'faddy eater'. Thoughts of the trouble Colin had probably taken in making the evening special, let alone its likely expense, almost distracted her from keeping up with their nervously charged conversation en route.

Soon they were turning into the expansive restaurant car park when Helen suddenly blurted out, "Ooh, I hope I don't let you down in here, Colin." He turned towards her with a puzzled frown, wondering whatever she could possibly have in mind. "Oh, Colin, I'm ever so funny with my food. I'm not at all ambitious in finer culinary circles such as this. I have to say I'm really very much a 'meat and two veg' sort of boring diner."

"Oh, is that all?" said Colin dismissively. "Be assured that meat and two veg is a house speciality in here. I wondered what you were going to say. I have to confess that I'd also been a little struck by what seemed to be your initial hesitation when I asked, on the coach yesterday, whether I would be able to see you again."

"I was really thrilled," Helen replied in a flash and with her compellingly broad smile, "that you wanted to see me again. I hadn't dared think that you might not. My hesitation though may well have been about something else." At this, she paused and swallowed hard. "I first needed to... well... I had to see someone named John and..." whereupon her voice lowered appreciably – "tell him that I would not be able to see him again."

"Oh heck! Are you otherwise in a relationship with someone then?" Colin uttered in another hushed tone, matching his lingering puzzlement.

"Not anymore," Helen replied, much more confidently. "I had to inform him though that I have met someone else. Anyway, our relationship was not really going anywhere. John had loads of other distractions. We can each thankfully draw a line under all of that now."

Colin didn't know what to say. It eventually fell to Helen to break yet another vacant pause. "Come on. Shall we go in? I'm dying to taste some of those exotic specialities."

They spent another memorably enjoyable evening. The restaurant stoically acceded to taking Helen's shamefully limp request for 'very well-done fillet steak' – and a little salad – effortlessly in its stride. She need not have worried at all. By the time the evening had drawn to an early close, written large at the top of their notional list of next steps was that of 'having to do it again sometime'. That prospect was never going to be in doubt, and sometime soon. Its most pressing part would be finding an evening that Helen could confidently accommodate among her unforgiving policing shifts.

"Wahey!" roared Ivor Axford, as Colin meandered early – or so he had thought – into the Intake team room on the following Monday morning. "How did the Sammy jollies go then, Teach?" Ivor added in his customary exaggeratedly sarcastic tone.

"They were exceptionally good actually," Colin replied with a passive smile. "You would do well to put yourself forward, Ivor. At the very next opportunity in fact," he suggested, lifting an unenviable pile of post and other material from his heaving in tray.

"Yes, I'll certainly need to bear that in mind," said Ivor much less passionately, and without looking up from what he was otherwise doing.

Annie Wrigley, along with Glenda, also appeared within minutes. They were each, in contrast, much more sincere in their greetings at seeing Colin returned safely to the fold. He proffered a series of variously positive headlines from the handicapped holiday though without, of course, any particular reference to Helen Harrison.

It then fittingly occurred to him to let Cora know that he was back. As he headed along the corridor towards her office, a familiar and almost welcoming plume of bluish smoke drifted from her open door. "Well, good morning, Colin," she chirped in her customary welcoming vein, "glad to have you back on board. How did it go?"

He found himself moving into what was now beginning to feel like a familiar précis of holiday headlines. While this was received with an evident degree of genuine interest, Cora had – perhaps typically Malone – already heard of the death of the woman who had been taken ill en route. Furthermore, and to Colin's considerable satisfaction, she had also received glowing reports from Jim Rathbone about Colin's sterling contribution to the week's success.

"Anyway," she said, changing the subject, "get yourself acclimatised back into the real world, before sparing me half an hour on various bits and pieces. I'm in all morning and I could do with getting up to date with you on various matters arising." Colin assented to this suggestion with a nod and returned to the Intake team room where duty calls were already coming in thick and fast.

"How've things been here, then?" he said to Annie, having now more or less got his breath back.

"Well," she said in a decidedly ponderous vein, "the Grattage family, now minus Tommy of course, have really hit the headlines. They had, some considerable time ago it seems, received a notice to quit from the council for chronic rent arrears, without of course letting on to anybody. This notice has more recently been invoked, if you please. June and the kids will be moving into Scotch Corner Lodge tomorrow, if we can confirm transport arrangements.

In other respects," she went on to say, "Maggie has made an impressive start in mobilising June. The top and tail of that though has been largely about establishing very basic routines and making limited inroads towards consistent care of the kids. She's nowhere near to exploring the family's budgeting. The notice to quit came right out of the blue, without any forewarning to us! Cora though, bless her, now has the housing department firmly in her sights and incendiaries have recently been heading in their direction on a number of successive occasions."

"Phew," Colin grimaced, with uneasy pangs of self-consciousness. He of all people, during his much longer association with the family, must have shamefully failed to even contemplate the plainly obvious subject of their budgeting. That said, he thought, the ways and means of engaging with June, and particularly Tommy for that matter, in any of those more delicate aspects of family affairs would be well worth seeing.

"I have to confess to not getting round to any of that," he said forlornly to Annie. "So perhaps their move to Scotch Corner could be the right move in the longer term. They will be less of a moving target there and more likely to benefit from the orchestrated involvement of its staff."

"That could well be true," Annie acknowledged, "though reducing their rent arrears will itself be no mean feat in beginning to restore any equilibrium." They each then turned independently to other priorities.

Colin set about returning calls made in his absence and looking through reports received from typing, before filing them away methodically. Although there was still considerable material to plough through, much of it seemed mundane, so he thought it perhaps better to link up with Cora to begin prioritising pressing jobs to be done. He soon found himself reacquainted with the familiar aroma of smoke as he headed towards Cora's office.

"Come in and shut the door," she announced brightly on spotting him hovering politely on the threshold. Stubbing out her cigarette, she smilingly proclaimed, "Right then, Colin, first things first. How would you feel about attending further handicapped holidays later in the year?" Colin faltered momentarily, wondering whether Cora's acutely tuned data reception might have somehow beamed in on any hint of romantic liaisons.

Playing it poker-faced, however, by saying how much he felt he had gained from the experience of working with disabled people, he was immediately struck by how hollow that assertion must have sounded. So, turning abruptly away from interview mode, he tried to suggest more casually how he would well consider taking part in further handicapped holidays on some future occasion. "There may be other more pressing skills to acquire though in the shorter term." At this, he then, again feeling awkward in wondering whether Cora might still be delving mischievously here, he added emphatically, "Such as mental health work for instance."

"That's okay then," Cora added with an element of finality, "I'll happily play that card should Jim come back to me with another craving plea for your services. Let's move on. Has Annie yet had chance to bring you up to speed on the Grattages?"

"Indeed she has," Colin replied. "I'll really have to get quickly back on track there. I had no inkling of rent arrears."

"No, you won't," Cora returned abruptly. "That poor woman's had to put up with far too many changes in recent weeks. We'll not be saddling her with any more. Annie and Maggie are making some headway, in spite of the current crisis, and they can concentrate now on seeing that through. We will then be handing it all over to a long-term team to steer the family through Scotch Corner and beyond. In some respects, that should have happened long ago."

Colin could not help feeling somewhat taken aback by this no-nonsense approach by his supervisor. He wondered if Cora was still put out, or at least disappointed, by what may have been his failings surrounding the Grattages being plunged into their current depths of despondency.

"Did I miss something there, Cora?" he uttered mildly.

"Well, if you did, Colin, we both did," she replied firmly yet kindly "Not all your work, however, nor indeed all of mine, is singularly our individual responsibility. While we, of course, have important professional responsibilities to maintain, make no mistake, we are otherwise constituent parts of a much broader service. It is one that has to work alongside other service providers. Whatever shortfalls may have befallen the Grattage family, they are likely to have been partly the product of not entirely faultless inter-agency communication. In a family such as theirs, communication chains are endless. Goodness knows where the probation service and others have been – together with us of course. The challenges are infinite. We all have to work together better."

There was a pregnant silence, eventually broken unsurprisingly again by Cora saying, "I have a much more searching question to put to you, Colin." He met this with another of his puzzled looks. "There's a senior social worker post coming up at the Chatterton office over the next few weeks," she announced. "Might you be at all interested?"

Colin was taken aback. This really was something out of the blue. He didn't know what to say, before eventually spluttering, "I-I really hadn't given any thought to anything like that… not at this stage, Cora… it's not been something we've really talked about."

"Well," said Cora, still kindly, "we seem to be talking about it now, don't we? What do you think then?"

On recovering from the shock, Colin gradually became more composed. "As I said, Cora, I've not yet had occasion to think about anything like that. Perhaps more to the point, do you think I should?" Cora pursed her lips thoughtfully but without saying anything.

"Do you think I'm really ready for anything like that?" he winced enquiringly.

"Well no, not really. Not yet," Cora replied confidently, "but I really do think this is something you should be thinking about and, more importantly, working towards. Applying for this post now, in at least acquiring interview experience, could do wonders in steering you full steam into an upward line of travel."

"Oh, right then," said Colin, obediently. Cora thereupon picked up the phone and eventually spoke to someone in personnel to set the ball rolling on Colin's behalf.

"You'll probably get a letter within a week or so," she said curtly, replacing the receiver. Before returning to his office, Colin explained to Cora that he had taken the liberty of acceding to Elizabeth Winstanley's request to accompany her to the initial review of young Ellis Bott.

That name needed no introduction. This was a young man who, as Colin explained, had recently been committed to local authority care following extensive involvement in a spate of burglaries. Cora needed no reminding of Bott's prior acquaintance with several Intake workers, including Ivor and Colin, following isolated episodes of relatively minor misdemeanour.

Colin then moved into something of a Rathbone-like commentary in acknowledging how Elizabeth had more recently taken longer-term responsibility for Ellis's case on his being committed to care. The court had clearly taken a serious view of the young man's escalating offending behaviour. It had consequently increased the 'tariff' at its disposal by making him the subject of a care order to the local authority.

Among a limited range of placement options that happened to be available to the authority, Ellis had been duly admitted to a community home some considerable distance away, St Vincent's, on the Welsh border. Elizabeth had had limited opportunity to get to know him beyond what was contained in his file, and this had been where she had been struck by Colin's reference to a young man who he found to be 'a likeable rogue'.

"Well, yes," Cora observed. "A day out with Elizabeth Winstanley should certainly keep you occupied," she said, glancing at him over the top of her spectacles. "That's fine, of course," she confirmed. "Your contribution on young Bott's behalf may be the least he deserves in his current circumstances. I'd be interested in you letting me know what the review makes of him."

Back at his desk, Colin returned to an unrelenting pile of papers begging attention. To his increasing dismay, it appeared that even more items of post had since been added to the task. At the top of the pile, however, was something that really caught his eye.

It was a letter written exceptionally badly, in blue biro and an untidy scrawl. Printed in bold type, in the top right-hand corner, was the name and address of the local remand centre. Turning over the page quickly to reveal its author, Colin discovered that it was from Tommy Grattage. Of all people, this was addressed to 'mrmilwud'.

Despite its starkly simple and illiterate format, the letter otherwise spoke volumes. It was an expression of Tommy Grattage's profound apology for the harrowing episode he had recently inflicted on Maggie and Colin in the family home. "*tel the yung lady imreelysori if I scaird her*," it said. "*I was not getting at ither of you but i new I wud be going down agen any tim soon. Hop you can forgiv me. Im ever so sori.*"

"How's that then," Colin gasped audibly to himself, "for restoring any wavering doubts about the solace of human nature?" It certainly gave him considerable incentive to drive on effortlessly in sorting out his other bits and pieces. I'll need to show Tommy's letter to Cora and Maggie, he thought. Oh, and Annie of course.

Colin's musings were then sharply interrupted by a tap on the door and a familiar voice calling his name. It was Elizabeth Winstanley, in all her glory and with her familiar smile. "Back from the seaside I see?" she said. "How did it go?"

"Much better than I'd been expecting actually, Elizabeth," he replied, almost matching her beaming expression. "How are things with you?"

"All the better for seeing you," she chimed. "I've just popped in to confirm our forthcoming date. Are you still okay for Ellis Bott's review on Thursday?"

At this, Colin felt just a touch uncomfortable. He wondered if any waning in his smile might have given any mixed messages about their, thus far hale and hearty, but otherwise arms-length familiarity. Actually, he didn't know what to think. The delicate prospect of Helen Harrison now making a huge impact on his feelings – or even on his life – was tipping most other things upside down.

Quickly recovering his composure, Colin confirmed his availability for the review. "Are you driving or me?" he asked, in a now more business-like sort of way.

"I'd be grateful if you would," Elizabeth replied meekly, though Colin could not bear to notice if she might have been fluttering her eyelashes. "I really don't relish driving all that way again, just yet," she added.

"That's fine," he said. "I'll see you Thursday then." Now, in other circumstances, he might have previously been inclined to ask Elizabeth where she lived and whether he could offer the option of his picking her up from home. While in some ways that still remained a compelling thought, Colin rather decided to remain business-like. He said he would meet her at the office and they would aim for an 8.45am departure, if that were okay of course. It was duly agreed.

"One important early lesson though, Elizabeth," Colin added swiftly. "Try not to address young Bott as 'Ellis'. He detests it. He's more commonly known to the wider public as 'Eli' – and even to nearly everyone at a couple of local schools he hardly ever attended."

"Oh, right," Elizabeth acknowledged thoughtfully, really appreciating this prompt. A measure of self-doubt imbued her having failed to discover any of that during her introductory visit to St Vincent's to meet 'Eli' and when studying his file – or so she thought. She realised she was perhaps on something of a learning curve in matters relating to the Botts. "I'll look forward to seeing you early on Thursday then, Colin," she said cheerily, sweeping gracefully through the door.

Colin returned to his admin sorting in preparation for a likely busy week ahead. He mentioned to Annie and to Glenda in passing, as they each dashed in and out of the office, the substance of Tommy Grattage's letter. He also showed them just how moving he had found the sublime simplicity of Tommy's badly written words.

Annie and Glenda readily tuned in to Colin's telling sensitivity. He was, however, somewhat less inclined to share any of that with Ivor, when he later returned to the office. Ivor had a distinct propensity, or so Colin thought, for riding roughshod over any expressions of emotional warmth, particularly for those who Ivor would sometimes refer to as 'the criminal classes'. All of that seemed to Colin to be a strange, if not incomprehensible, position for a social worker to take.

Driving home, his thoughts unsurprisingly returned to Helen. She was on 'lates' that week, involving 'two to ten' shifts and therefore it was likely he would not see her again until the weekend. He couldn't resist making a circuitous detour homeward via the town centre that represented a major part of Helen's 'beat', just on the off chance of seeing her. In the event, however, he was out of luck.

Before imminently getting back on track with his own casework priorities that week, Colin had to deal with the impact on him sparked by Tommy's letter. Spurred on by that incentive, he decided to call Nick Gibling, Tommy's probation officer. On picking up the phone to make the call, Colin smiled as he brought to mind Cora's earlier sentiments about the probation service. It also occurred to him, as he waited to be put through to Nick, that he could not quite understand why he had not previously taken the trouble to initiate this sort of liaison with that service.

"Hello there, Nick," he said cheerily, on being put through. "I just wanted a word about Tommy Grattage, if that's okay"

"Oh, yes," returned the probation officer dolefully, whereupon Colin enthusiastically explained recent events surrounding the letter. "Oh that's interesting," Nick observed in a continuingly half-hearted way, falling well short of Colin's spirited explanation. The probation officer said nothing further, possibly waiting for Colin to elaborate.

When Colin explained that he felt inclined to visit Tommy to thank him personally for taking the trouble to convey his sincere apologies, Nick became arguably more responsive – albeit to a minor degree. "You'll need to put a request in writing to the remand centre for a visiting order," he explained, before falling silent again.

"Oh, right then," Colin acknowledged, and, in an attempt to try to bolster further dialogue, he inquired, "How's Tommy doing, by the way?"

"Don't really know," replied Gibling, maintaining his blank tone. "I certainly haven't heard anything and I doubt if I'll get to see him until nearer his release." There was little else to say apparently, or so it seemed. It caused Colin to wonder whether this particular probation officer – or perhaps even the wider service he represented – may not have held local authority social services in any particularly high regard.

Nevertheless, Colin thanked him in spite of the stilted nature of their exchange. The entire episode merely served to suggest that Cora's remarks may not have been too far misplaced. It had not really been a fervent example of inter-agency co-operation.

Colin's week thereafter appeared to fly. This was in spite of his enforced separation from Helen, since duty continued to call, thereby limiting them to intermittent lengthy phone calls, albeit, of course, on a daily basis. Beyond that, there was also plenty of work for Colin to do – including office duty – and much to catch up with on cases he had not been near for well over a week. If all of that were not enough, he was then dealt something of an additional double-whammy.

A letter was duly received at home confirming Colin's invitation to attend an interview three weeks later in connection with the senior social worker post at Chatterton. On bringing this proudly to Cora's attention on the following morning at work, she additionally informed him that he had also secured a place on the much-anticipated, and indeed much-revered, forthcoming mental health course.

This would represent an important step towards equipping Colin to undertake formal mental health assessments, particularly in the more critical aspect of work conducted on behalf of people potentially requiring compulsory admission to hospital. While this had been something that he had previously observed others undertaking, it remained an area of the generic role in which Colin required further training. It really seemed to be just one thing after another, when all he really wished to do was simply catch sight of Miss Harrison again.

Then, as he was beginning to digest all of that, he found himself preparing for yet another early start to accompany Elizabeth to Eli Bott's review. They each arrived at work in plenty of time, before encountering one another by chance in reception. "What time are you picking me up then, Colin?" Elizabeth said, in that now familiar mildly suggestive way with its knowing smile.

"Oh, as soon as humanly possible," he quipped in subscribing to the spirit of what he evidently now regarded as just a bit of harmless fun. "I've just got a couple of calls to make and I'll give you a knock on the way down."

"Ooh, get you," Elizabeth retorted in an overly exaggerated way that reinforced for him the superficial nature of their playful banter that might just have began to wear somewhat thin. Then she added in a much more purposeful and professional way, "We can compare notes with one another en route and try to anticipate how we might co-ordinate our respective perspectives in reporting to the meeting." Colin nodded in agreement as he hurried to his desk.

Cora happened to catch sight of him as he scurried past her open door. "Slow down, Millwood, and just try to concentrate on the job!" Colin chose to say nothing as he hurried along.

THIRTEEN

Mixed feelings

AS THE TOLEDO SPED from the office, the two social workers only traded in minor elements of superfluous banter in the best interests of young Bott. Nevertheless, they could not avoid common exchanges early on. Colin was struck by how much more relaxed he now felt in Elizabeth's company and how strange it seemed that his past awkwardness on seeing her had somehow evaporated.

Before immersing themselves in analysing how astutely the Botts conducted family life, early chatter meandered over a range of simple topics: where they lived, the haphazard nature of their circuitous routes into social work, how they each found the ups and downs of working at the Longley office, and, inevitably, upon the reliable option of each other's forthcoming holiday destinations.

"Conrad has a weird fascination with the Baltic," Elizabeth uttered passively, and largely to herself, gazing into the road ahead.

"Conrad?" Colin interjected.

"My better half," Elizabeth added, with perceptive enthusiasm. "We've been together since university," she smiled. "He's a law lecturer at Keele," she swooned, clearly unable to hide her admiration.

This brought Colin a wave of blithe relief. "So then, Elizabeth," he began, at last switching the focus responsibly towards Eli Bott, "how do we play our respective roles today?" They each then shared their individual perceptions of Eli: Colin from past associations, Elizabeth from more recent encounters, which fortunately arrived at broadly similar evaluations. Speeding along, they made good time through Leominster and beyond.

Colin was favourably struck by his colleague's reference to Eli having been made subject to a 'section seven' care order. This specific detail about relevant legislation was not necessarily a common feature of social work dialogue. It caused Colin to wonder if this indicated the extent to which his colleague really knew her stuff, or whether she was merely relying on the veneer of what she may have casually read somewhere.

For now, that was immaterial. In no time at all, the Toledo was turning off a minor road, to crunch noisily along a weaving gravel drive. This eventually opened out to reveal the grand red-brick façade of St Vincent's. Its imposing splendour struck a rather fitting chord as a self-assured educational establishment – and one not uncommonly found among those catering for young people in care.

Any passing reference to St Vincent's being a school were reliably associated with it having previously been an

Approved School. The 'school' label had doggedly persisted via custom and practice, especially among those working there. It was also cultivated in part by the organisation aspiring towards scholastic ambitions to attract those local authorities seeking more discerning placements. This was in spite of subsequent legislation disposing of the approved school label in favour of the modern concept of a 'community home with education'.

What St Vincent's actually prided itself upon – unbeknown to Colin and Elizabeth on first acquaintance – was its reputation as a setting where rural isolation contrived to manage, or rather actively discourage, young people's inclination to abscond. Rural isolation, of course, implicitly inspired any number of additional qualities among organisations craving prestige, including the potential for wide-ranging character-building activities. These could well have each been viable considerations in the local authority identifying St Vincent's on Eli Bott's behalf and not, as Colin had first assumed, of it perhaps representing the only vacancy that happened to be immediately to hand.

Having announced their arrival at the school office, Colin and Elizabeth were escorted along a wide, grandiose wood-panelled corridor containing fine paintings of rural life. There were also portraits of important-looking dignitaries, who may have had past associations with the school. Colin impishly wondered if St Vincent himself might be among them, though chose not to enquire. A profound silence was broken only by their echoing footsteps, as they dutifully followed their guide.

They were eventually met by a pervading aroma of furniture polish when shown into a small room that was fitted from floor to ceiling with bookshelves, and was otherwise dominated by an imposing long-case clock. Here Colin and Elizabeth were asked to await being called into 'Bott's review'. It was apparently one among a sequence of reviews held that morning. The silence and the smell of polish remained all-encompassing and were continuously accompanied by the monotonous ticking of the clock.

Two people eventually came out of the adjacent meeting room with serious expressions. Colin assumed that they were likely social work staff from the review scheduled prior to Eli's. "They didn't seem too jolly," Elizabeth whispered, before they each settled down to listening to the clock again.

They were eventually shown into a spacious room with fine furnishings, where a number of people were seated silently around a wide rectangular oak table. A large man in a tweed suit promptly stood to introduce himself as the head of the school. He welcomed Colin and Elizabeth cordially, before introducing others present. They each variously represented a range of educational and care staff, along with matron of course, together with a dour middle-aged woman. Her foreign-sounding name Colin found difficult to determine and she was said to be the resident psychologist.

This was very pointedly a meeting comprised exclusively of professionals. Colin had been wondering all along where Eli and his parents might have been in all of this, but now, looking around this solemnly assembled gathering, he was easily persuaded that Ted and Jean Bott, let alone young Eli, were probably well out of it. The head went on to explain, however, that Ellis would be invited to attend the latter part of the meeting, to hear its recommendations.

This was clearly an early initiative to reflect upon Ellis's recent arrival in placement and to devise early plans on his behalf. A member of care staff was accordingly invited to summarise early perceptions of the young man. There was unsurprisingly little to report beyond tentative observations around his early engagement with staff and others. The point was made, however, of Ellis quickly appearing to latch on to older boys in his 'house', boys 'from Birmingham' no less, who would unlikely represent positive role models.

Colin found this summary, in postulating Ellis to be 'easily led' a rather premature finding, but he did not comment for fear of it turning out to be patently true. It could have indeed been a feature of his spiralling offending history that had brought him there. In other respects, Colin felt, this was a young man thrown into a completely foreign environment. It was perhaps of little wonder that he might crave any element of acceptance or familiarity among others, in forging an understanding of these strange surroundings. Colin therefore found this to be a disappointing introduction, devoid of promise – let alone encouragement – at such an early stage.

His wisely keeping his counsel on any of that, however, turned out to be a good move. Elizabeth was invited to give an overview of events leading to Ellis's arrival at St Vincent's.

Her summary was articulate and faultless, in speaking of a warm and loving family whose positive influence appeared to have been repeatedly undermined by the behaviour of a child who was an entrenched 'school refuser'.

That, she went on to explain fittingly, became the beginning of Ellis seeking acceptance elsewhere, arguably among peripheral acquaintances, rather than among those who he might have more reliably regarded as friends. It was this, she suggested, that may have generated an inclination to experiment in minor misdemeanours, before graduating towards aspects of more serious delinquency.

She explained how the juvenile court had taken a dim view of this latter pattern of offending and how this had inevitably led to their making a section seven care order. "His family are thoroughly ashamed of him," she concluded. "None of them has ever been in this sort of trouble before."

"Anything to add, Mr Millwood?" the head asked, from the chair.

"Not a great deal," Colin replied. "My colleague's largely said it all." Colin had noted intriguingly how Elizabeth's oratory had cleverly incorporated some of his own earlier observations made on their journey that morning. "I had some involvement with Ellis," he said, "during his introduction to IT – intermediate treatment – at an earlier stage of his offending history, along with others on our team," without bothering to mention Ivor by name nor Cora's passionate interest.

"Working with him one-to-one," Colin continued, "on things he happened to be interested in, could be quite rewarding. Unlike lots of the other lads, who would just generally be mad about football, Ellis couldn't bear it. He detests everything about the game. He is rather into fishing, in a big way, and if only someone could be troubled to take him fishing all day, he would be absolutely in his element. Burglary would never enter his mind. I would also have to say in conclusion that, in many respects, I've generally found Ellis to be a likeable young man in spite of all the difficulties in which he now finds himself."

"Hmm… that's an interesting thought," the head surmised. He went on to explain at length more of St Vincent's professional approach. This interestingly incorporated a glowing account of inescapable past achievements. It extended to matters concerning the granting of 'home leave', which Colin thought had unfortunate echoes of being in the services, and how fortnightly home leave could be forfeited within the recognised tariff of 'consequences' in managing young peoples' negative behaviour.

Social services, it was explained solemnly, were responsible for organising transport arrangements for any leave. Family members could also visit the school, at certain times, though responsibility would necessarily fall to them in first establishing that any proposed visit would not clash with planned school activities.

Beyond other miscellaneous exchanges of familiar details, the review moved towards its anticipated conclusion. Ellis was then brought into the meeting along with his key-worker, whereupon he beamed at seeing two familiar faces from Longley. His key-worker, who sat dutifully by his side, looked barely any older than Ellis. The head moved into a suitably edited précis of information considered by the meeting.

Sadly though, it was not at all pitched at a level that young teenagers with limited verbal understanding were likely to grasp. The head then asked Ellis if he had any questions or anything further that he might wish to say. Ellis immediately froze at being put on the spot. He exchanged quick glances with his key-worker, who gave an encouragingly nodding smile. Ellis, however, silently shook his head. Much to his apparent relief, the review was at an end. Ordeal over.

Once outside, away from the wide arc of serious-looking adults and in the relative sanctuary of the room with the ticking clock, Ellis looked slightly less perplexed. He briefly exchanged exaggeratedly feigned swinging punches with Colin in a playful way, albeit at Colin's instigation. "How's it going then, Eli?" he asked.

"I don't like it, Mr Millwood. I want to go home," he replied.

"Yes, I can understand that," Colin said sympathetically, "but you have to give it time. This is an order made by the court no less and for reasons that should not be difficult for you to understand, surely?"

"I still want to go home though," Ellis said, with a degree of finality. The two social workers spent some time consoling him in a supportive way, emphasising the prospect of family visits and of home leave. All of that, alas, felt as hollow to Colin as it must have inevitably sounded to Eli. Elizabeth tried valiantly to lift the gloom by promising to make another visit to St Vincent's within the week.

"We've all got to work at it," she said, tilting her head characteristically to one side in that expression of sincerity.

The key-worker, who turned out to be named Glyn, deftly took the cue in adding encouraging observations. He mentioned how Eli's current downturn was a common setback for many young people who eventually overcome the distress of being away from home. "Enjoy it when you can and while you can," he said, "and make the most of opportunities on offer." Eli's forlorn frown spoke volumes of not being at all reassured. He lowered his head in silence.

It also occurred to Colin that, had Mr and Mrs Bott happened to attend this meeting, their departure at this point would have likely heaped even more acute sadness on the lad. With very mixed feelings, the two social workers bid farewell. Eli's brief wave prompted Elizabeth to reiterate her promise to see him soon.

It was fast approaching lunchtime as they crunched their way back along the drive. Colin suggested stopping on the way home for a quick bite to eat. Elizabeth readily agreed as they began to exchange sundry observations about their morning business. Mixed emotions appeared to overlay it all.

On passing through Kington, Colin suggested stopping off in Hereford. "Fine," Elizabeth remarked. "I'm game for anything." This caused Colin to wince inwardly, though he thought it better to just ignore any hint of innuendo. He accordingly took the road via Mancell Lacy towards Hereford. There they found a quaint pub near the city centre where they enjoyed a relaxing light lunch and mulled further over their meeting at St Vincent's

"Have you ever been to Hereford before?" Elizabeth eventually asked. Colin admitted that he had not. "No, neither have I," she mused. "It's home to the Mappa Mundi, isn't it?" Colin had no idea what she was talking about. His puzzled, vacant stare prompted her further elaboration.

"The Mappa Mundi," she emphasised, and went on to explain, "is an ancient map of the world, or at least of how the world was understood to have existed in the thirteenth century. It's said to be a national treasure." Colin was increasingly struck by his colleague's apparent wealth of knowledge. Perhaps she was not just a pretty face. She may have had more insight into section seven care orders after all.

"Should we go and seek it out then?" Colin suggested. "By the time we get back to Longley our working day will be as good as over. Neither of us will be this close to Mappa Tuesday, whatever it is, any time soon."

"Mappa Mundi," Elizabeth reiterated. "That's actually a jolly good idea, Colin. I might have known you would somehow be worth bringing along." At this, they unashamedly took their time in concluding a relaxing lunch before heading off on foot towards the cathedral.

They were not to be disappointed. From the moment they entered the imposing edifice, each became absorbed by the splendour it contained. Wandering idly beneath Norman arches, they each meandered separately, deep in their own thoughts, towards various items of individual interest that happened to catch their eye.

At length, emerging from their awesome musings, they found themselves leaving the Chapter House garden, to eventually encounter the enthralling highlight of the Mappa Mundi. How they marvelled at the splendour of this iconic calf-skin treasure from so long ago. Time simply ebbed by as the two colleagues eventually wandered, almost in reverent silence, towards the cathedral library and archives.

"Hey," exclaimed Colin, glancing at his watch on reaching the bright sunshine of Cathedral Close, "look at the time!" Quickening their pace, they headed towards the car. They were almost surprised to find it where they had left it, at what seemed such a long time before. In other respects, however, they had nothing to rush back for. The afternoon was well advanced and there would be no way of returning to the office before the end of the working day.

By the time they eventually reached the outskirts of Longley, traffic was beginning to crawl, conforming characteristically to the advent of rush hour. A sombre stop-start procession was gathering all along Broad Oak Road when Colin suddenly exclaimed, "Good God! Was that Eli Bott running into Millets Lane?"

Elizabeth was shaken starkly from the mist of a semi-trance. In desperately gathering her wits, she was not exactly sure in which direction this particular lane was to be found. Colin, however, was already engaged in precariously negotiating a right-hand turn across the unforgiving stream of oncoming traffic. He then, having performed a hurried three-point turn in a side street, rejoined the slow Broad Oak crawl impatiently back again, towards Millets Lane.

There, in contrast to the main road, all was quiet. Only a young girl was to be seen delivering evening newspapers. Driving slowly along each side of the lane, they peered closely down every possible exit from the road. Nothing. Colin had to question whether he had actually just seen young Eli. *How can that be at all possible?* he wondered.

There was no alternative but to first return to the office to enable Elizabeth to collect her car. Colin took this opportunity to let himself inside the building to use the phone. A handful of social workers, Annie Wrigley among them, were still there finalising aspects of last-minute work before heading home. "Blimey," said Annie, looking up to see Colin, "you're late back. What kept you? Nothing to do with Elizabeth Winstanley I don't suppose?"

"Well, not really," Colin answered falteringly, "but other things perhaps. I think Eli Bott may have got back here before we did. I need to have a word with the duty senior." Annie could see that Colin was palpably perplexed. She went to put the kettle on.

To Colin's considerable relief, the emergency duty rota indicated that Malcolm Miller was the duty senior that evening. He and Colin were familiar voices to one another on the duty circuit, though they had never met in person. In this vein, therefore, Malcolm was extremely receptive and supportive of Colin's doleful tale of woe – given, of course, that Colin's hapless sighting of Eli had yet to be confirmed. "We'll not go looking for him though,"

Malcolm said confidently. "We'll play it by ear and respond accordingly should any information come our way."

"I wouldn't mind taking him back," Colin uttered, largely by way of atonement.

"That's good of you to offer," Malcolm replied, "but you can consider yourself off duty now, Colin. If Eli crops up tonight, be assured that we'll see to him and I will let you know about it in the morning. So, we may speak later," he said, kindly but finally, before ringing off.

Malcolm's reassuring sentiments turned out to be of little comfort to Colin. Throughout the evening, he found himself continually turning over in his mind inescapable misgivings about the harsh realities of Eli's distant placement. It was almost getting in the way of his being able to look forward avidly to the end of Helen's week-long late shifts and to the prospects of seeing her again.

Then, perhaps in the proverbial context of great minds thinking alike, Helen rang him quite out of the blue – primarily for a catch-up and really to make arrangements for their seeing one another over the coming weekend. He was considerably encouraged to hear that this was evidently on her mind too. Colin, however, could not forego any opportunity of relaying to Helen details of recent twists and turns surrounding the latest episode of young Eli Bott.

He arrived early at the office on the following morning – or so he had thought – only to find Elizabeth's car one of three that were already there. Karen's bright and breezy, "Morning, Colin," as he hurried inside, was followed by a not-uncommon cynical remark from admin staff about how he must have just fallen out of bed.

Popping his head around the door to Elizabeth's office, Colin found her already at her desk. She was studying case notes carefully through spectacles perched precariously on the end of her nose. He could not resist the casual quip of saying, "Not the latest update on Mappa Mundi, I don't suppose?"

Elizabeth looked up startled, before smiling, "No such luck, I'm afraid. Nothing's changed on that front." Then she added in a more serious vein, "Malcolm Miller rang first thing though. Apparently the police picked up young Eli late last night. Being well known to them, they were aware of his 'care' status. So, when they happened to see him casually on the street last night, they immediately regarded him as being at large. He was promptly apprehended and taken into custody.

"Duty social workers by the name of... er," glancing down at her notes, "Dorcas Clewes and Melvin Allen apparently took him back to St Vincent's without any difficulty at all. It seems that Eli had managed to wander unnoticed off the premises, not long after his review, before promptly hitching a lift in this direction. He must have been well on his way while we were idling round Hereford. Don't worry though, Colin, I'll be speaking to the school any time soon."

Colin sat motionless on returning to his desk, bemused by the spiralling nature of this episode, in which social workers had been consigned to merely minor roles. So much for St Vincent's being hot on absconding then, he thought to himself, and not forgetting what dire consequences might have heralded Eli's return to placement.

As other team members began to arrive, generally hailing bright "good morning"s, Colin consciously pulled himself together to turn his attention to the day's other priorities. Not least among them was that of his at last seeing Helen again later on. That of course became yet another distraction.

Those relatively hushed early beginnings of the Intake team's working day were then broken by a round of voluble cheering. Ivor Axford was scurrying towards his desk with a gloating, "Wa-hey then, have you heard the one about the kid who got back home from his far-away review before the social workers who had gone there to see him?"

Although Annie and Glenda were among a handful of people who did happen to know about it, they had not been inclined to mention it and certainly not in Ivor's company. Colin fittingly ignored Ivor's not-untypical sarcasm. There was, after all, a child's welfare at stake in all of this. So he said nothing, rather marvelling at Ivor's astute intelligence network and doggedly fixing his gaze inanely on an unimportant piece of paper in front of him.

FOURTEEN

Conflicting needs

THE WEEKEND COULD NOT come quickly enough for Colin. Not just in terms of putting any dismal reminders of Eli behind him, but in his at last being able to see Helen again. His mood had been so troubled by what he regarded as another fiasco surrounding Eli that he hardly dared to winsomely presume that Helen could really be his one true love. Taking that for granted, he thought, could well compromise an ecstatically promising relationship.

His deep thoughts were suddenly broken by the shrill ringing of the telephone. It was Helen, of all people! She sounded remarkably eager as was he, in confirming their arrangements to see one another. Since Colin needed little prompting on that score, he was not long in showering and changing in plenty of time to collect her. Arriving at the Harrison door in seemingly no time at all, it occurred to him how broad a smile he happened to be sporting.

"I'm not sure I should be speaking to you," Helen announced solemnly as she swung open the door.

"Why ever not?" replied Colin, feeling distinctly weak at the knees at the worst thoughts of compromise feverishly coming to pass.

Helen's face beamed as she impishly replied, "Our woman inspector, Pamela Pendleton, has fallen out big style with Doreen Levitt." Colin immediately recognised this latter reference to the social services area officer for the local district covered by Helen's police division. He had also understood from Helen how these two women, Pamela and Doreen, had long been the best of friends and how their enduring association had crucially bridged not unfamiliar tensions between their two services.

"What's sparked that, then?" asked Colin.

"Don't really know," came the reply. "It has something to do with what social workers must have done, or not done, I think. I just heard Pamela say to Doreen, 'Paperwork? What paperwork?' as she slammed down the phone."

"Hmm…" mused Colin. "Nothing would surprise me there. I'm only glad that you might still be speaking to me though."

"Course I am," she said, planting a firm kiss on his cheek.

That set the scene for an absorbing evening, along with dinner of course – not forgetting characteristically well-done steak and generous heaps of fresh salad. It pre-empted their resolve to make further arrangements to spend all of the following day together, in Dovedale no less.

Its tranquil rural setting managed to eclipse any daunting distractions of work for both of them. It was sheer bliss.

On returning home much later that evening, Colin picked up mail that had lain idly on the mat since early morning. Among items of junk mail was an envelope sporting the local authority logo. Feverishly torn open, it revealed an invitation to attend a forthcoming interview for the senior social worker post at the Chatterton office. Sitting down to read it several times over, in absorbing the reality, Colin could hardly take it in.

Arriving early for work on the following Monday morning, being on office duty was only one incentive for such a prompt start. He was also eager to share his interview invitation with Cora.

"Blimey, Colin," Karen chirped from reception as he dashed in. "We weren't expecting you just yet," before adding with a hint of sarcasm, "the cleaners have only just left."

"Oh, I'm part of their sweeping-up detail," he sang in reply, as he dashed upstairs. "Just polishing things off."

To his disappointment, even Cora had not yet arrived, so he found himself at an unusually advanced state of preparation for office duty. As other team members arrived at intervals, he remained hesitant in sharing any hint of his interview news, considering it fitting to first inform Cora. In doing so, however, he was inwardly dreading the prospect of Ivor having heard about it and his making loud, exaggerated announcements on arrival.

Fortunately perhaps, and for whatever reason, Ivor did not make an early appearance. Glenda was Colin's duty colleague that morning and their shift got off to an unusually sluggish start. The morning was turning into something of an anti-climax as far as he was concerned. At length, however, he was suddenly shaken from his idling by his ringing telephone. Pam announced the name of a caller from the local council 'for the duty officer', and Colin immediately invited her to put them through.

Colin introduced himself cordially to the caller. The voice from the other end avoided any complimentary resort to such considerations and just blurted out, "We've got a man here going mad. He's livid that his daughter's been tattooed without his permission."

"Yes," said Colin, intentionally passive and implicitly inviting elaboration. There was, however, only a vacant pause.

"His daughter's only fifteen," the caller eventually said, in a continuingly exasperated tone. "He's going ape-shit here and wants social services to do something about it."

"What is he – or whoever – expecting social services to do?" Colin asked, trying hard to maintain a courteously helpful approach. It was not at all clear who, or indeed which particular council department happened to be on the line.

"It's abuse," the caller replied in desperation, and, at this, Colin began to figuratively sit up.

"Okay," Colin pursued. "Go on." He purposely avoided any immediate enquiry into the child's identity at this early stage.

"Look, mate," the caller went on, now more appealingly, "he wants you to do something."

"Yes, but what?" Colin proffered. Following another vacant pause, Colin added obliquely, "Pardon me for perhaps appearing unduly inquisitive here, but where might I ask has this child actually been tattooed?"

"Well," came the reply somewhat falteringly before clearing his throat to add, "I-I think it was somewhere in Fenport."

"I was actually referring to the location of the tattoo," Colin said, unavoidably smiling to himself, and with a degree of emphasis. "But, if this fifteen-year-old has been tattooed without parental permission, irrespective of where it might have been, that could also be a matter for the licensing authority along with the tattoo studio."

"Well, we are the licensing authority," came the reply, in a now more confident air, "but father says it's child abuse."

"We would need to know much more about what has actually taken place, and on what particular basis the man is maintaining it's abusive. If his daughter has simply been tattooed without parental permission, then that legitimate concern is a matter for the licensing authority.

"If, however, he is complaining about an intrusive location of the tattoo on his daughter's body, then that could, of course, have further implications involving this department, and indeed the police. So far though, you have not really said anything to me that is clearly something for social services to act upon; not yet at any rate. If there is any doubt, this man could be advised to approach social services directly."

With that, the caller rang off. While Colin braced himself in fully expecting a call back, nothing more was heard. What's more, Colin was not at all sure what he could possibly write down in making any meaningful record of the conversation that had just taken place.

As he pondered further upon it, he noticed that the usual amount of daily post had been deposited in his tray. Among routine papers, he encountered two particular items of interest. One was a visiting order from the regional remand centre. The second item was an invitation to attend a forthcoming course of mental health training assigned to equip staff to comply with the advent of new legislation.

This prompted Colin to go in search of Cora again to bring her up to date with each of these important developments. To his relief, her door was now open and she waved him in to take a seat. Following her bright and breezy greetings – simultaneously stubbing vigorously into her ash tray – Colin reported on each recent aspect of good news.

"Annie's in the process of handing the Grattages over to someone on the long-term team," Cora observed. "You would be well advised to let the new worker, Monica, know about the context of your trip to see Tommy, at least out of courtesy. In other respects, June is regrettably not making the progress we might have anticipated, in spite of Maggie's support, alongside that of Scotch Corner staff. So-o," she sighed, "the prospect of care proceedings may well be re-emerging."

A pregnant pause had them each dwelling upon mutual thoughts.

"Hmm…" Cora eventually murmured. "Interesting."

Then looking quizzically down towards her desk, she avoided any direct eye contact before casually asking, "And where do you see yourself in five years' time?"

"I'm sorry..." Colin replied, shaken suddenly from thoughts of the Grattages.

"Where do you see yourself in five years' time?" Cora repeated firmly, now fixing her gaze directly upon him. "Come on, Colin, this is serious stuff. You cannot possibly contemplate attending an interview without giving due consideration to pressing matters of career development." At this, she smiled sweetly at him.

"Oh, I see," said Colin thoughtfully, realising that Cora was pitching into interview mode. "I will need to give that some thought," he said. "At this stage though, you may need to allow me to apply the overnight test to the substance of my reply, if that's okay?"

"It's quite okay," she said, still smiling, "but it's something we must return to in our very next supervision, next week in fact."

"You're on," returned Colin with a note of finality, heaving himself out of his chair to return to duty officer priorities.

Back in the Intake office, Colin took the opportunity of letting Annie know of his interview news. He was also keen to know of the progress – or otherwise – that June was making. "She's evidently more limited in her understanding than we may have first imagined," Annie observed. She went on to echo Colin's own perceptions, "While there is little doubt that she loves her kids, she probably fits the mould of someone who can only cope with one child. Competing needs of more than one child are just too much for her to handle."

"What should I say about any of that to Tommy when I see him?" Colin grimaced.

"I don't think you can," Annie replied firmly. "Monica, the new worker, will need to reappraise the progress the family is making, perhaps with renewed emphasis, before arriving confidently at any informed opinion. It's not for you. Just tell him that everything is being done to support June and the kids right now, as best we can."

Two days later, Colin found himself on a typically congested M6, on his way to the regional remand centre to visit Tommy. Crawling along parallel lanes of sluggish traffic, with frequent stops and starts, he eventually saw the imposing outline of the prison in the distance. Leaving the motorway exit, Colin was struck by the sombre silhouette of darkly etched prison walls against the backdrop of a bright blue sky.

On arrival, he double-checked his readily accessible visiting order and identity card as he made his way towards an imposing, boldly designated main entrance. A loud bell quickly prompted the brisk opening of a small sliding gated window in the huge wooden door. Another silhouette, this time of a uniformed peaked cap, was quickly revealed through the tiny aperture.

Colin announced his name and position, together with the local authority he represented, "To visit Tommy Grattage." The peaked cap evidently consulted a prepared list of that day's anticipated appointments, before noisily sliding the aperture firmly shut. Almost simultaneously, a single door within the wider wooden structure was swung open and Colin duly stepped inside. That, too, immediately closed behind him with a loud bang.

Before Colin was able to turn around to make eye contact with the gatekeeper, the silence was broken by the prison officer announcing curtly, "We don't need you bastards in 'ere."

Colin was taken aback. Before he could muster any sort of coherent response, the prison officer proceeded to unlock an inner door to reveal a wider reception area. Without further ado, he added dismissively, "This place is full of 'do-gooders'. It's all just meat to us."

"Oh, right," was all that Colin could say as he strode through the second door. Here he found himself at a counter largely dominated by an extensive wire grille which maintained further elements of gated security. Colin was required to sign-in and empty most of the contents from his pockets, which were placed into a locker for safekeeping, and for security of course.

Another prison officer presented himself to Colin, who explained that he would be escorting him 'to Grattage'. This second official was appreciably more personable. He enquired via routine pleasantries about the visitor's journey that morning, whether this was his first visit to the establishment and so on.

As they made their way along a couple of further echoing corridors, Colin was silently reproaching himself for not taking at least a more quizzical line with the first officer on the 'bastards' front. He then comforted himself on the basis of it likely being futile, not least in terms of any such retaliation probably achieving little. In any case, that opportunity had long since passed.

Colin was eventually shown into a smaller room, where he found Tommy Grattage seated patiently, with his arms folded, at a small table and in the company of yet another prison officer. His escort explained that the other officer would be required to remain present throughout the visit that would have to be restricted to forty-five minutes duration. For his part, however, Colin had not expected their business to take anywhere near that long.

He greeted Tommy warmly, to which Tommy barely nodded in recognition. "How are you doing then, Tommy?" Colin asked, maintaining his bright and enthusiastic approach.

"Well, how do you think?" Tommy responded coldly, with an undeniable hint of sarcasm. "This ain't exactly the Grand 'otel yer know."

Colin winced inwardly at the naivety of this crass beginning. He felt increasingly out of place in such an unfamiliar, oppressive setting. It caused him to wonder whether the foreign nature of these surroundings was somehow undermining his capacity to relate meaningfully to people – to a prisoner no less – and not forgetting Cora's now prophetic reference to engaging effectively with 'an angry man'.

Taking a seat, Colin said, almost apologetically, "Tommy, when I got your letter I just had to come and see you. I had felt all along that your manner that day, when Maggie and I came to see you, was not the Tommy

Grattage that I was beginning to get to know. I could not help feeling that something else was troubling you and caused you to react so angrily. I genuinely just wanted...", whereupon he paused in trying to find the right words, before simply adding, "well, I just wanted to understand it. And now of course, I realise what it was."

"So," he went on, still struggling somewhat and coming close to repeating himself, "I just needed to set the record straight with you. I was so pleased to receive your letter. Maggie and I really appreciated you taking the time and trouble to express it in the way that you did. I just wanted to, well, say thank you to you personally, Tommy."

"Good God," exclaimed Tommy, sitting upright. "I thought you'd come over 'ere today to 'ave it out wi' me! What, no 'ard feelings then?" he uttered, almost in exasperation.

"None at all," came the reply. "We now understand the pressure you must have been under at the time."

"And I'd 'eard the council were goin' to kick us out the 'ouse," Tommy added dejectedly.

Colin was relieved to hear that the family's eviction was not proving to be another unanticipated shock to Tommy. "Well," he said, "that was something else that we had not known about until late on. June and the kids are now in temporary accommodation where they are getting plenty of support."

Colin winced inwardly again at this vain attempt to somehow dilute the entrenched nature of the family's current predicament, within an insipid concoction akin to exaggerating any hint of progress they were making – or not making – at Scotch Corner. "Another social worker, named Monica, is helping them now," he said encouragingly, "along with Maggie of course."

"Glad yer came ter see me," Tommy observed forlornly. "Don't get many visitors."

The primary nature of Colin's visit had obviated his even contemplating the merits of bringing anyone else along. Quite apart from negotiating the terms and conditions of visiting orders, he was not inclined to contemplate the logistics of including June – with or without any of the kids. That would be something for Monica to consider, he concluded, not to mention how indeed Tommy would relish residing at Scotch Corner.

"Is there anyone you might wish to see?" Colin asked largely out of courtesy.

"Nah!" Tommy replied, before adding by way of afterthought, "Riggo pr'aps, cos 'ave only gorra few weeks t'do." At this, Colin inwardly wished Monica and her team all the good fortune they would need, let alone the Grattage kids.

He eventually bid Tommy a genuinely fond farewell, before being escorted back towards the entrance near the main gate. Having retrieved his pocketful of possessions, Colin was mildly disappointed to not encounter the officer who had gone to such lengths in welcoming him so warmly that morning. This perhaps reflected his inability to reconcile himself with not taking a more assertive line at the time over the crass reception he'd received on arrival.

He soon found himself heading back to Longley, this time along a much more free-flowing M6, which had him reaching the office in next to no time. As he entered reception, Pam called out to say that Tom Shone had been looking for him

Tom was a member of one of the long-term teams. He was an older chap who had worked for many years in the old mental health department and was widely acclaimed as an experienced professional in that field. Keeping largely to himself, he fraternised little with other colleagues – many of whom were much younger – and showed little incentive for 'small talk' in preferring to confine himself to his specialist caseload. The new wave of generic social work had yet to ebb as far as Tom. This, however, was a mantle he wore with pride, and to considerable admiration throughout the wider professional network.

Beyond common courtesies, Colin had unsurprisingly found few opportunities to engage professionally with Tom. He could not therefore remotely imagine why Tom had been looking for him. It took a degree of searching before Colin eventually found him, tucked away in a confined office adjoining the larger team room containing Tom's more generically inspired colleagues.

"Oh, hello, Colin," Tom beamed courteously on seeing him. "I've been looking for you," he said, standing to shake his hand.

"So I gather," Colin replied with a smile and a hint of anticipation.

"Well, the word's got around that you're on the list for a forthcoming mental health course," Tom announced. "It so happens," he went on to explain, "that I have been asked to conduct an assessment for a compulsory admission this afternoon. So, I wondered if you might care to accompany me in an observational capacity – just to see what it's all about. Though I can tell you it was Cora who actually approached me about it."

"I'd love to," Colin said enthusiastically. "Just tell me where and when." They agreed upon the arrangements for meeting up in the early afternoon. Colin returned to his desk with much anticipation of actually witnessing Tom Shone in action.

He thereafter reflected further with Annie upon his visit to Tommy Grattage, and how genuinely remorseful Tommy had appeared about his previous encounter with Colin and Maggie. Annie was just in the throes of reminding him to bring Monica up to date on all of that when the in-rushing Glenda – ferrying another delivery of bacon sandwiches – proved too much of a distraction for much more sensible discussion.

Tom Shone was later explaining to Colin, as they made their way to his car, much of the somewhat limited background to the circumstances that he had been asked to attend. It concerned a young man, named Basil Richards, who apparently had no previous mental health history. "That in itself is interesting," said Tom, "and, of particular relevance to your forthcoming course is the fact that the medical team in this case are doing this one by the book. We begin by having the two necessary medical recommendations for Mr Richards' compulsory admission to hospital. That, of course, conforms fittingly with the spirit of the new legislation. It doesn't always work like that though in common practice, I can assure you."

Colin was aware of certain elements of the new 1983 Act and the expectations that legislation placed upon the role of social workers in certain circumstances, particularly in considering patients' compulsory admission to hospital. Social workers necessarily had to be 'approved' in formally discharging necessary responsibility for this critical aspect of the admission process. Colin duly hoped to acquire that approved status through the upcoming course he was looking forward to attending.

In preparing for the course, he had taken opportunities to observe other colleagues undertaking mental health assessments. Those experiences had tended to suggest, in Colin's limited view at any rate, that the process was not always driven by the wisdom of exact science. This opportunity, however, with Tom Shone no less, somehow had every prospect of being different.

Tom went on to explain how Mr Richards had been referred to the local psychiatric hospital by his GP. This had followed an allegedly deteriorating episode in his mental health, which had coincided with episodes of anger and aggression towards his wife. The couple also had a three-year-old child. The psychiatrist and the GP had each provided medical recommendations for Mr Richards' compulsory admission to hospital, for assessment at least, and possibly for treatment. This was in accord with Section 2 of the Mental Health Act 1983.

"So then, Colin," Tom posed en route, "what are we endeavouring to establish on this visit?"

"Well," said Colin, who had been fully expecting this trip to comprise only of a spectator role as far as he was concerned. "Phew, I suppose we need to establish whether this chap should really be in hospital," he concluded in a half-hearted, uncertain vein.

"Hmm," Tom muttered, "but we've got two written recommendations from doctors – the chap's GP, together with a specialist responsible medical officer no less – who are each unequivocally saying that hospital is where he should be."

"Yes, we do," Colin admitted, almost shamefully embarrassed at overlooking such an elementary factor, before suddenly announcing, on the penny having dropped, "but because the man may need to be detained against his will in the interests of his own health and safety, or rather in this case, with a view to the protection of others."

"Spot on," said Tom, with a hint of triumph, as they sped towards the patient's given address. That turned out to be a flat, recently acquired in fact by Mrs Richards. It was later said to be a considered means of sanctuary for herself and her daughter in the wake of her husband's increasingly unpredictable behaviour. The family home was otherwise an isolated farmhouse on a distant border of the local authority.

It was Mrs Richards who answered the door, welcoming Tom and Colin warmly. Upon the social workers being shown through to the living-room, they encountered Basil Richards sitting motionless. He said nothing in response to their greeting. Their three-year-old daughter was said to be with her grandmother, who lived nearby. Basil evidently had what looked like remnants of porridge in his hair. Home circumstances in the flat were otherwise warm and comfortable

Tom opened the meeting by announcing that Dr McNiven had asked the social workers to visit. Basil Richards remained silent, maintaining his gaze averted elsewhere. "How are things with you right now, Mr Richards?" Tom enquired kindly. There was still nothing.

Mrs Richards endeavoured to interject before Tom managed to stall her interruption with a silent shaking of his head. He needed, of course, to confine his conversation at this point with her husband. Maintaining his kindly tone, he asked Mr Richards how he was feeling. Met by continuous silence, Tom resorted to asking whether there was anything troubling him.

At this, Basil Richards looked up, but not towards Tom, before uttering vacantly, "Well what it was… was…" That was it. His averted gaze resumed and his taciturn manner prevailed.

Tom then turned his attention towards Mrs Richards, but before he was able to pose any further question, Basil Richards suddenly rose to his feet and rushed out of the room. With Colin in delayed pursuit, Basil entered the bathroom on the opposite side of the small hallway, whereupon he promptly locked the door. All went quiet.

Mrs Richards recounted a series of recent episodes to illustrate aspects of her husband's increasingly strange behaviour. Tom later attributed this, at least partly, to the likelihood of paranoid ideas and possible auditory hallucinations. Further questioning through the locked bathroom door, intermittently from Mrs Richards and

Tom, each enquiring if Basil was okay, failed to evoke any response. There was no sound from within.

Some considerable time elapsed before it was eventually established that Basil was, in fact, no longer in the bathroom. He had evidently made good his escape at some juncture through the first-floor window! He would have then had ready access to his car. There was no indication of where he might be. The social workers felt at least obliged to ensure that Mrs Richards was safely lodged with her parents, along with her daughter, for fear of her husband's agitated return to the flat.

They then set out to the family farmhouse. This was the only possible lead they had in establishing where Basil Richards might be. The property was unsurprisingly shrouded in darkness. While they acknowledged that this futile gesture had limited prospect of locating Basil, it was something that had to be eliminated. It simply proved to be the dismal outcome of Colin's so promisingly anticipated 'fly-on-the-wall' insight into approved social work practice. It culminated no further than the anti-climax of witnessing Tom lodging formal documents – his own application for the patient's admission to hospital, along with the two accompanying medical recommendations – at the hospital admission ward, in anticipation of any subsequent intervention on Basil's behalf.

"Right then, Colin," Tom probed as they drove back to the office, "any reflections on all of that?"

"Well," Colin pondered, "I'm not really sure what headway was able to be made to determine any informed social work assessment, or really what actual evidence we had that the patient was a danger to himself or to other people."

"That's a fair point," Tom acknowledged, "but to start with we have two doctors unequivocally saying he may have a mental health disorder and that he should be hospitalised for assessment and, if necessary, for treatment."

"Okay," acknowledged Colin, "but what about his being a danger to himself or others?"

"While I have to acknowledge that we only have his wife's assertion of his anger and aggression," Tom replied, "on the other hand, we do have a chap here who's just jumped through a first-floor window. In the midst of all this uncertainty, are we prepared to just wait and see whether this, albeit alleged, anger and aggression eventually become targeted towards his three-year-old child? In many ways, an inter-disciplinary assessment is only just beginning."

"Hmm," acknowledged Colin, turning towards Tom and smiling. "That's true enough. Just think what the newspapers might make of that."

Basil was eventually taken to the admission ward several hours later, having been picked up in the town centre by a police patrol.

FIFTEEN

Applying the science of the patently obvious

COLIN FELT REALLY FORTUNATE to have any number of further opportunities to shadow Tom Shone. This went some considerable way in his beginning to grasp the essence of better-informed mental health practice. Practical insights fittingly coincided with the advent of his long-awaited Mental Health Act training. Much of his 'sitting by Nellie' involved Colin accompanying Tom on routine visits to clients with a known diagnosis. Three-fold aspects of the social work role largely incorporated providing sensitive support, alongside implicit monitoring of patients' general progress and by encouraging positive interaction with other people.

Occasionally this would cause Tom to alert other health service staff about aspects of patients' treatment, usually around medication. Broader elements of the supportive role seemed to focus on reaching out to individuals who became increasingly isolated by their illness. Since others in the wider locality would be inclined to give well-known patients a wide berth, this often consigned those individuals having to find other ways of coping with the stigma this label often brings.

It was work that also included dealing with unforeseen crises from time to time, graphically portrayed of course. People already known to the service could be prone to acute episodes of relapse in their psychiatric condition. Emergencies would similarly extend to people previously unknown to local psychiatric teams apparently manifesting acute symptoms for the first time, for any number of reasons.

In this vein, calls to the Longley office made on the basis of someone possibly requiring compulsory admission to hospital were usually referred directly to Tom Shone. People refusing the offer of hospital, for any reason, including those arguably associated with their state of mind, could be potentially placing themselves, or indeed other people, at risk of harm. This would then become a pivotal factor leading to exclusive consideration by a social worker of their need for compulsory admission. This was usually referred to simply as someone being 'sectioned', thereby acknowledging active recourse to particular sections of mental health legislation.

Appreciating the finer detail of these requirements was a primary focus of specific Mental Health Act training, for social workers expressly selected to undertake that work. It had acquired renewed emphasis on implementation of the 'new' Mental Health Act of 1983. This was the training in which Colin had been actively engaged. Central to its objectives was the opportunity for course participants to work alongside experienced social workers, like Tom Shone.

On this basis, compulsory admission requests received at Longley inevitably resulted in Tom spontaneously alerting Colin to offer further opportunities of 'sitting by Nellie'. Having an eager recruit was evidently something that encouraged Tom and evoked a perceptible hint of pride. While there would inevitably be occasions when Colin was otherwise engaged, and hence unavailable, he too was generally keen to take advantage of all such opportunities to enhance his appreciation of mental health practice.

Mental health work, however, would often cause Colin to regret how the intractable association of high drama – that in itself could specifically define the compelling need for someone's compulsory admission – had an unfortunate capacity to haphazardly stereotype an individual long afterwards. Not only did it undervalue the impact of crisis upon that person, it could also cruelly hasten their spontaneous transition to the alarming and indelible profile of a 'mental patient'.

If that were not damning enough, news of the factual detail of certain dramatic episodes could cheaply extend to the amusement of others. These were after all human beings – Colin would occasionally lament to Helen – whose own professional experience in this area of work was from yet another perspective. Basil Richards had, for instance – and to Colin's enduring dismay – attracted a certain amount of notoriety around the office as being 'the chap who jumps out of upstairs windows'. Little account was given, so it seemed, to the acute distress that could drive someone to even contemplate such action.

Similarly, the long-standing mental ill-health of one sixty-two-year-old Rosie Watkiss had widely earned her the reputation around Longley as someone who was married to Jesus Christ. Few, however, could have had any idea of the much lesser-known depth of Rosie's chronic self-neglect, nor indeed of the extent to which this heaped unrelenting anguish upon her married daughter.

It was with much of this newly acquired experience that Colin, driving home from the office, began to turn his thoughts towards his forthcoming interview for the Chatterton post. That then became something that acquired increased momentum upon his opening a typed envelope he found on the front doormat. It was, unusually in his experience, from the training section at social services headquarters.

To Colin's immense joy, and let alone considerable surprise, this contained news that he had successfully completed his Mental Health Act training. He barely had time to let it all sink in before the phone rang. It was Cora. He recognised her voice without any need for introduction.

"Tried to catch you before you left the office," she announced. His heart sank. Phone calls at home from Cora just had to be about something serious.

"Go on," he replied tentatively, holding his breath.

"Just wanted to congratulate you," Cora returned brightly. "You're an approved social worker. Well done."

"I've only this very minute opened my letter from training," he replied almost breathlessly.

"It's very well-deserved," Cora said. "While rumour has it that you already had it comfortably in the bag, it became 'set and match' apparently on Tom Shone's glowing commentary of your potential in that area of work. And that comes, of course," Cora added, "from someone who is hardly ever heard to volunteer any opinions beyond those on behalf of patients."

At that point, there was very little that anyone else could possibly add. The two of them chatted briefly in this encouraging vein before ringing off. Congratulatory greetings subsequently drifted in from several quarters over the next couple of days.

Then Colin returned inevitably to thoughts of his forthcoming interview. Preparation, he surmised – particularly for an Intake post – had to go well beyond implementation of the mental health legislation, irrespective of all its complex challenges. A much wider scope of local authority priorities was continuously driven by an ever increasing professional agenda and not least from an unforgiving public.

Headlines were increasingly generated, or so it seemed, particularly from London boroughs, about children continuing to lead miserable lives. More chillingly, these would sometimes culminate in their painful deaths at the hands of those charged with caring for them. Two four-year-olds, albeit from different boroughs over a period of a matter of months, had each died at the hands of step-parents. One, who had in fact been technically in the care of the local authority, was said to have been seen only once by their social worker in ten months. Another, similarly murdered by her stepfather, was said to have been the subject of a complaint that a senior NSPCC inspector had failed to investigate.

All that gave Colin cause to ruminate seriously about aspects of his own practice. He wondered to what extent very evident failings in distant London boroughs could be replicated much closer to home. The Grattages, of course, quickly came to mind, before recollecting certain other children from memorable duty shifts.

While he readily acknowledged how the science of the patently obvious should not be so readily overlooked, instant recognition of any child's immediate circumstances tended to be restricted to the product of acute crisis. Day to day contact, on the other hand – particularly from an Intake team perspective – tended to generate more piecemeal opportunities for making informed judgments about any individual child or family. Then again, he reminded himself, that's where the mandate to work with other agencies applies.

Such was the complexity of intra-family relationships that they often tended to consign confident analysis by outsiders to the enigma of haplessly trying to see round corners. At this point, Colin felt that such deep reflection was becoming far too complicated. He would return later to interview preparation. There were much more urgent distractions on which to concentrate – largely thanks to Helen Harrison no less.

In no time at all, he found himself knocking on Helen's front door. It swung open and immediately sparked a long-lasting, enduring embrace. Colin then suddenly lurched back his head, looking inquisitively at his one true love before asking, "Do you actually approve of me?"

"What on earth do you mean?" Helen replied quizzically and firmly.

"Well," he said, in a quietly confident air, "I have to tell you that you're actually looking at an *approved* social worker no less."

"Wow!" Helen exclaimed, almost with a squeal, as she pulled him towards her to hug him tightly. "When did you hear?"

"Little over an hour ago," he replied, before explaining further as they set off arm-in-arm to spend yet another blissful evening together.

The following day, back in the office, Colin was back down to earth taking duty calls. While there were few matters of any particular substance, he and Glenda – duty partners for the day – found themselves lurching continuously, and a touch disappointingly, from one minor query to another.

All along, Colin had been eagerly anticipating the prospect of seizing half an hour with Cora, in connection with interview preparation. Anything like that though was prosaically forestalled by Cora's familiar absence elsewhere. Then, out of the blue, from the office window, he noticed her car gliding into the car park.

Just as he was preparing to leave reception, to ask Glenda if she would mind covering his half-hour diversion with Cora, Pam, with the phone at her ear, piped up, "Acting Sergeant Phillips at Elmington Police Station for the duty officer, Colin."

"Can Glenda take it?" he asked, almost pleadingly.

"No, she can't," Pam virtually sang in reply. "She's with one of the home helps in the interview room. I can tell you though that the boy he's talking about is not known to us. Father is though, but only as a Blue Badge holder."

"Oh, go on then," he said, slightly irritated. Dashing upstairs to his phone, he puffed, "Put him through."

At this particular moment, Colin struggled to reciprocate Sergeant Phillips' hale and hearty greeting. "Got a good one here for you," he virtually trilled with glee. "Mr and Mrs Charlesworth, from Thames Drive, Elmington, are refusing to have their fourteen-year-old son, Neil, back home after he'd been missing for three days."

"Had he been reported missing?" Colin asked promptly.

"No, he hadn't," came the similarly swift reply. "It's thought he's been staying with friends, as he's done before. It was in fact a parent of one of his friends who brought him here, when the Charlesworths said they wouldn't have him back. One of our policewomen has been round to see them, but all to no avail. They are adamant. This further episode is apparently the last straw as far as they're concerned."

"Is Neil known to the police?" Colin asked.

"No, he isn't, as far as I can see," Sergeant Phillips said.

"Do you mind hanging on to the lad?" Colin asked. "While I go round to see what's what, and with a view to encouraging a change of heart."

"We've already tried that," came a now more assertive reply. "It's not an option and he doesn't need to be here."

"While I'm with you on that one," agreed Colin, "and, for all we know, he probably doesn't need to be anywhere other than at home. The last thing we need to be doing is shipping him from one inappropriate place to another."

"Can't you put him in a children's home or somewhere? Or with foster parents even, just while you make your enquiries?" Sergeant Phillips asked, now slightly more appealingly.

"I have no authority to do that, and, at this stage, certainly no reason to be seeking any," Colin replied firmly, and just managing to avoid audibly stressing, "one damned fool place for another."

"Make it quick then," Sergeant Phillips snapped upon this insistence. "We don't have surplus staff here to keep kids entertained all evening."

"I fully appreciate that, thanks," Colin said, amicably adding as he rang off, "I'm on my way now." Hurrying through reception, he briefed Pam quickly on the matter in hand, asking her to inform Cora as he dashed to his car.

It was not far short of the end of the working day when Colin arrived at the family home. The detached stone cottage struck Colin as a somewhat unfamiliar destination for social work visits, at least in his experience. There he spoke initially to Neil's mother, Carol Charlesworth. Also present was the maternal grandmother – recently arrived from Leicestershire to accompany the family on holiday the following day – and two younger half-sisters, Elspeth and Tara. Two-year-old Elspeth clung tightly to her mother like a koala, constantly vying for spontaneously rewarded affection. Mr Charlesworth arrived soon afterwards, having taken the dog for a walk.

Mrs Charlesworth, an articulate woman, explained that she had moved to this address four years or so beforehand with her two sons, upon marrying Mr Charlesworth. The boys' names had subsequently been changed by deed poll. The elder one, Simon, aged eighteen years, had since moved on to live independently. Mrs Charlesworth said she had separated from the boys' father when Neil was eighteen months old. There had not been any subsequent contact.

She then, upon being joined by her husband, related a catalogue of Neil's deteriorating behaviour over the past two years. This had included vandalism at school, frequent deceitfulness, theft of money from home and his going missing without explanation "when it suits him."

The couple each related different strategies they had tried to influence Neil's 'better behaviour' and a series of professionals they had consulted. They appeared to have appreciated most the advice from education welfare, though the nature of any appreciable difference this had made was not really specified.

"What particular advice proved to be most effective?" Colin felt obliged to ask.

"Well, about us being consistent," Mr Charlesworth replied. This sounded to Colin that Charlesworth was merely blustering at this point, and perhaps intending to imply that nothing they were otherwise doing was in any way misplaced.

They then went to some length to demonstrate how it was not they who were at fault, whereupon Colin began to wonder if they might be protesting too much. He managed to temper, however, any inclination to jump too readily towards likely conclusions, quickly recollecting his own recent doubts about piecemeal judgements at an early stage.

The Charlesworths went on to say that Neil was really no problem at home with the family. He related quite well to his younger sisters. It seemed problems arose when he was out of the house. Mr Charlesworth then interjected by saying that he was currently banned from eating with the family because of his unacceptable behaviour elsewhere. At this, Colin swallowed hard in again quelling any hint of hasty conclusions. Then, not for the first time in this sort of exchange, he later regretted not querying at the time the intended effect of that redress upon the specific misdemeanour. "Surely", he thought to himself, "they were two completely separate entities".

Mrs Charlesworth said that they had even gone as far as considering separation in restoring an element of positive change for Neil, before deciding that was really taking things too far. Mr Charlesworth went on to reaffirm that he was adamant in no longer allowing Neil in the house until he could demonstrate that things could be different. Colin wondered how possible it would be for the Charlesworths to quantify any positive change for the better if Neil was actually required to live elsewhere.

"But I had understood," Colin interjected, "that Neil had been missing from home of his own accord?" He sought to make that distinction with a frown.

"I'm saying this now," Mr Charlesworth stressed, "after this latest episode."

This caused Colin to suspect elements of vindictiveness in the way Charlesworth might readily resort to means of punishment, as distinct from adopting composure in finding kindly ways of influencing changes in Neil's behaviour. Presumably, this distinction was not mooted by education welfare. Colin resisted any further inclination to enquire of ways they might have otherwise attempted to reach out towards Neil in the wake of all this. He also, at this early stage in a three-way discussion, resisted playing the potentially decisive wild card of asking Mrs Charlesworth if she still loved her son.

All that may have caused him to subsequently regret a handful of missed opportunities arising from this interview. Harking back to a familiar extract from Cora's figurative bag of interview tools, he remembered that of encouraging social workers to expressly bring to mind key objectives of visits they were about to make to interview clients. These, she would emphasise, should remain at the forefront of one's mind upon approaching the home address and before even knocking on the door.

"Come on," he said to himself. "Get a grip!" He was still trying hard to avoid evidently loaded questions in merely subduing the respondents to obtuse realms of defensiveness. He did, however, go as far as insisting upon Mrs Charlesworth accompanying him to the police station to see Neil. She willingly agreed, though this meant of course that Elspeth would have to cling along as well, since she could not possibly allow her mother out of her sight.

Neil notably showed no pleasure on seeing his mother arrive at the police station, unsurprisingly with a tightly-clinging Elspeth and a social worker. He remained sullen, in spite of Colin going some way to speak reassuringly and amiably to him. Reassurances, however, that he was not in any trouble – at least from a police perspective – made no difference. With his chin remaining on his chest, he said nothing. Any hope and expectation that Colin might have had of Neil's mother perhaps putting her arm around her dejected son were now sadly too much to expect.

This unhappy and disconsolate young man, Colin felt, was yet another far cry from the typical fourteen-year-olds social workers expected to meet in police stations. Eventually, when pressed further on what he would most like to happen, he said he wanted to go home. Colin's glimmering hopes at that point were again stalled by Mrs Charlesworth announcing, "No, that won't work. Nothing will change."

"So, where would you expect your son to go from here?" Colin asked.

"He'll have to go into care," his mother said coldly, with a hint of neither regret nor emotion. "We're supposed to be going on holiday tomorrow you know." Colin said nothing in reply, pointedly allowing a pregnant silence to at least make a point. He felt that holidays, of all things, from this young man's point of view, in the depths of such despondency, were sublimely irrelevant. Going on holiday could hardly be seen as the number-one priority in all of this.

Since it was by then six o'clock, Colin quickly excused himself to consult the on-call duty senior about the prospect of an imminent foster placement. To some glimmer of relief, however, amid this turgid episode, the senior for the evening happened to be Bernard Dobson. The two of them had become acquainted on the recent mental health course where they'd mutually been able to bask in the glory of success.

Bernard was eager to oblige Colin in his quest. He quickly came up with the names of Mr and Mrs Goulding as likely foster carers in being agreeable to step in. For Colin, this indicated that the tide could perhaps be beginning to turn for Neil Charlesworth. The Gouldings were experienced foster carers, well-known to out-of-hours staff – including Colin – for their ability to meet acute needs in emergencies.

More to the point though, for Colin at least, these foster carers lived within a quarter of a mile of the Longley office. He rang them directly from the police station to explain the unanticipated downturn that had befallen the young man in question. They were more than willing to oblige and said they would eagerly await Neil's arrival in due course. Colin stressed to them that it was also his abiding hope that Mrs Charlesworth would be accompanying them too. The experienced Gouldings were again more than happy at this suggestion. Taking it in their stride, they had seen it all before. All were welcome.

Back in the interview room, Colin found that Mother appeared to have made little, if any, headway in beginning to heal their rift. He explained to them his proposal for a short-term foster placement only, to afford family members something of a cooling-off period from this unwelcome episode. He pointedly avoided any mention of it facilitating the family's departure on holiday.

It was engineered, he stressed, to allow further preparation for the prospects of Neil's return to where he should be – at home with his family. This, he acknowledged to himself, was something of another hope rather than the anticipated product of any forthcoming assessment. It could just as easily pave the way for any agreeable alternative arrangements, whatever they might be.

Any anticipated assessment would need to explore a range of intra-family relationships and individuals' expectations. They would include several complexly interwoven issues: Neil's feelings about his change of name, his elder brother's view of family life and any associated factors that might have precipitated his living independently elsewhere.

It could perhaps even extend to exploring, and Colin continued to contemplate this with some feeling, to what extent Carol Charlesworth really did still love her son. While this may have not been the right time to ask, another central element to the assessment would be that of seeking to establish to whom Neil felt closest in his life. Colin otherwise avoided, at this delicate juncture, any hint of explaining to the Charlesworths about the prospect of their potentially being assessed for financial contributions towards their son's care.

By this time, Neil's mood was encouragingly appearing to lift. This had to be a central element of any short-term measures put in place for him and of exploring whatever options the future might hold. He accompanied his mother and social worker happily to the foster home. They were enthusiastically received there by Mr and Mrs Goulding, who helpfully took the lead in pointedly confirming arrangements for parental contact on the following morning, prior to the family's departure on holiday.

This implicit alertness of the Gouldings to getting this arrangement off to a flying start was exactly what was needed. Colin brought Bernard Dobson up to speed with this initial progress, though he anticipated having to brief Cora in greater detail the following morning.

SIXTEEN

Gaining interview experience

IT WAS ONLY ON arriving at departmental headquarters that it occurred to Colin that he'd never actually been there before. His one and only previous social work interview, for a trainee post some years previously, had been at the training office. How different the prospect of this imminent interview now seemed, for a management post no less. In spite of Cora's stoic assistance with preparation, he was still not exactly sure what to expect. He desperately hoped that he would not let Cora down.

Having been shown through to a waiting area adjoining the main reception, Colin was mildly surprised to not encounter any other interviewees. Taking a seat in an empty alcove, he began to turn over in his mind what little he happened to know about Chatterton. It was not really very much. He'd made the fleeting acquaintance of the area officer there, May Overton, at odd training events, but he had no reason to expect that she would know who he was.

It then dawned upon him that he had made something of a grave omission in terms of interview preparation. The previous holder of the post in question was one Ian Fullwood. Ian had been known to Colin from his university course and was clearly someone who he could have – and indeed should have – contacted in acquainting himself with purposeful insider knowledge. "Damn it," he uttered in an audible whisper. "How daft was that?"

The resuming silence in the alcove was intermittently broken by ringing telephones before a young woman appeared in the doorway to call Colin's name. "Are there any other applicants for interview today?" he asked as he hurriedly followed her along the corridor.

"Not half," she answered. "The panel's interviewing all day," she smiled. "You are number three on the list this morning, then it's mainly external candidates this afternoon." Colin's heart sank at the thought of that level of competition. The young woman then promptly stood aside to hold open a door into another office. There he encountered three people seated in a motionless line behind a low table.

May Overton's was the only face that he really recognised. The district manager, Mike Colburn, immediately stood to welcome Colin warmly, introducing himself as the panel 'chair'. Only then did Colin realise that he had in fact seen him before, albeit in passing somewhere or other. Mr Colburn accordingly introduced his two colleagues. Besides Mrs Overton, Audrey Billington was the third panel member. She was the area officer from the

Thursfield office, someone who Colin only knew by way of her widely acclaimed no-nonsense reputation.

The interview began with Mike Colburn explaining the familiar process that would follow. He smiled at Colin, adding softly, "We have noted with interest, Mr Millwood, your glowing reference from Miss Malone." This happened to be something that Colin had not in fact seen. The interview then began by Mrs Overton being invited to explain something about the post in question. The panel was clearly by then well into interview mode.

Colin suspected that this introduction was intended to put interviewees at some measure of ease. It certainly provided welcome breathing space, while simultaneously giving helpful factual information about the post. He took some encouragement from hearing how Chatterton acknowledged certain theoretical elements of Intake practice. This was, after all, a relatively modern concept within emerging social work methodology, loosely based on the application of crisis theory. The essence of that approach was something that Colin had gathered from Cora. It postulated how the provision of outside help in the midst of family crisis had the capacity to hasten people to find ways of overcoming those sorts of social and emotional difficulties more effectively.

There then followed a series of pre-arranged questions by each member of the panel in turn. This familiar format was well-developed. It endured timelessly, long before escalating popularity gradually emerged of candidates being first asked to give prescribed presentations to interview panels. The first question was easy enough for

Colin. It came almost instinctively from Mrs Overton, asking him to outline the ways and means of effectively managing an Intake team.

He was able to give an authoritative overview based on experiences shaped so diligently by Cora's enlightened vision. This was also timely in vanquishing early interview nerves, almost to the point of fuelling a modest hint of confidence. Colin was able to give coherent case examples across the Intake spectrum in illustrating how some of the challenges mentioned in Mrs Overton's overview might be tackled. These extended, as he pointed out, to determining those cases – with anonymous reference here to the Grattages – where short-term Intake methodology might not always represent the most fitting approach for families or workers alike.

May Overton smiled, with what Colin hoped was a hint of approval.

He went on to stress the benefits of a whole-team approach that thrived upon recognition of social workers' individual skills and experiences. He emphasised critical aspects of team leadership, including the benefits of learning from one another, though carefully not referring here explicitly to 'sitting by Nellie'. He spoke authoritatively of the continuing need for education and training, particularly in keeping practice up-to-date – mentioning in passing his own recent approved social work course – and in stressing the interplay between informal consultation and the mandate for formally managed staff supervision.

That confident appraisal appeared to nudge Mike

Colburn towards the cue of querying on what base cases can go desperately wrong. "Why is it that they falter?" he added, "even tragically, and what do we learn from them?" Colin winced inwardly at this tall order that lay unforgiving and motionless at the heart of social work practice. In orchestrating a means of organising his thoughts accordingly, Colin grasped eagerly at the common-place cricketing analogy of needing to keep one's eye on the ball.

He seized implicitly upon the notion of how unpredictable trajectories – indeed of cricket balls, and of family life alike – can be susceptible to all sorts of twists and turns. They are each subject, he suggested, to a whole range of influences: from someone's initial approach, purposeful or otherwise, to wholesale or even subtle actions of individuals, and not to mention how conspiring environmental factors sometimes generate implicit changes of direction.

"In family life, of course," Colin concluded, "the stakes are much higher, particularly in terms of professionals misinterpreting the ways and means of family relationships. They can overly rely solely upon what people say – that may or may not be true – or what they see or hear that may similarly be open to all sorts of exaggeration or misplaced confidence that all is well. First impressions need checking out."

"Can you elaborate on any particular instances?" Mike Colburn mused passively, without shifting his gaze from the papers on his knee.

Colin now felt somewhat put on the spot. His mind

went blank. He tried to locate something articulate to say in summarising the Grattage family, but alas, absolutely nothing came to mind. He looked down quizzically in front of him, frantically searching for inspiration, desperately hoping to avoid any utterance along the lines of "Er," realising that would abruptly undo him completely. Then, in a flash from nowhere, Maria Colwell came victoriously to his aid.

"Modern practice," Colin commenced, "has been sadly infected all too often by cases that have gone wrong. It has illustrated unforgiving details about children who have led unhappy lives and sometimes painful deaths." He went on to refer to recent history's tragic sequence of cases from the early 1970s with the death in Brighton of Maria Colwell.

He pointed out how that particular case had generated a major rethink of professional practice. At its outset it had led to the newly configured idiom of 'non-accidental injury', which became a searching mandate for professional agencies. This required contributing agencies to work much more effectively together in matters of child welfare. To this end, area review committees had been established to forge formal co-operative platforms for reviewing the management of serious cases.

Colin went on ultimately, however, to lament the evident shortcomings of this widely acclaimed rethink. Its aftermath had been perpetuated by even further tragic outcomes – in Berkshire, Brent, Lambeth and indeed beyond. These, he surmised, strongly emphasised that the lessons of Maria Colwell had not made the appreciable difference that had been anticipated. "More to the point, of course," he went on to say, "there could be no guarantee of these tragedies not being replicated much closer to home."

"And are you able to give any more specific lessons from these individual cases, Colin?" Mr Colburn asked.

While he was loath to admit that he couldn't really, not with confidence, he decided to bluff it anyway by relying on what little he happened to recollect by saying, "Well, the four-year-old in Brent was only seen once by her social worker in ten months. The review in Lambeth," he added, "regrettably found that the white social worker there was too trusting of the family, because they were black." This paper-thin elaboration was the most Colin could muster before bringing his answer to an abrupt stop.

Then, plainly by way of afterthought, he added, "There were, of course, in each and every case, recurring messages about the merits of effective staff supervision and management, and continuous access to professional training." This, however, was more of a safe bet rather than confident acquaintance with particular case histories.

"Thank you," Mike Colburn said quietly, while Colin winced inwardly at this limited delivery. May Overton continued to smile though. This caused him to wonder whether she'd found his painfully thin answer in any way amusing.

"Miss Billington," Mr Colburn then announced as he invited the third panel member to pose a question.

"Thank you," Audrey Billington acknowledged. After a brief pause she opened with a bright, "Good morning, Mr

Millwood. Could you tell us where you might see yourself in three years' time?"

Colin looked fleetingly through the window, uttering an inward 'Yes' in Cora's general direction towards Longley.

"Well," he said. "I would of course like to think of myself settled happily into this senior social worker role at Chatterton. While I remain committed to all aspects of generic social work, I'd also like to think that in due course I might, well… wish to specialise in one or another aspect of practice. At this point though I have no particular preference, but, having said that, I found my recent approved social worker training has inclined me very much in that direction.

"Then again, however," he continued, "I learned a great deal from my excursion on the handicapped holiday" – omitting any reference here to red buckets or police women – "and beyond that, the current emphasis on tackling serious child abuse brings increasing expectations of professional practice too".

"Beyond all of this though," it suddenly occurred to him, "I'm still a qualified teacher. Who knows what advances in social work education might have to offer in the fullness of time? The list goes on. Possibilities are endless and any future option could just as likely be generated by something unexpected, quite out of the blue."

Colin felt at this point that he was at last getting into interview mode, almost alongside the panel it seemed. May Overton continued to smile, so that restored at least an element of self-satisfaction. Then, somewhat to his disappointment, Mike Colburn announced, "Well, Mr

Millwood, that's about it from us. Would you care to ask us any questions?"

While Colin had anticipated the merits of finding something sensible to ask at this point, he wondered if he might have said enough, rather than prolong the process needlessly. Cordial thanks were uttered all around and Mike Colburn anticipated that candidates would be informed of the panel's decision within the following twenty-four hours.

As he left the interview room, Colin was immediately deflated upon seeing Derrick Jay sitting expectantly in the alcove. He was an older social worker of considerable experience, from another local office, who was vaguely known to Colin. Derrick was evidently next in line for interview. At this point, with nearly a whole day of interviewing yet to come, Colin felt that Cora's original prediction about where he might be in five years was ominously spot-on. *Oh well,* he thought, *I may have at least benefitted from a slice of interview experience.*

In driving back to the Longley office, he kept turning over in his head the questions that the panel had posed. Typically, on each such occasion, he was able to bring to mind various additional facts and interpretations that were there for the taking. *Blast!* he kept saying to himself, banging his hand on the steering-wheel.

On turning into the office car park, he realised that it was past lunchtime, but that was the least of his concerns. He had no appetite whatsoever. As he entered reception, Karen hailed a hearty, "Oh hi there, Colin," but not so much in her familiar jokey sort of way. Her subsequent,

"How did it go, then?" was in a much more sincere vein of genuine interest.

"Very mixed I think, Karen. They are interviewing all day would you believe? So I'll not be lying awake anticipating any phone call."

"If you don't get it, Colin, it will only go to prove that they don't deserve you," added Pam, in a similarly serious vein to that of her colleague. It made Colin swallow somewhat hard.

En route to Intake, Colin dreaded the prospect of a hale and hearty Ivor Axford on parade. He geared himself up for issuing a curtly unsavoury reply. As it happened, however, Cora's door was open. "We were not expecting to see you today, Colin. You've got other fish to fry," she retorted as he hovered in the doorway. "How did it go then?" she added.

"Oh I don't know, Cora. Very much a mixed bag, I think. That said, they are interviewing all day so I'm not getting any hopes up."

"It's the experience that counts," his senior replied. "Whatever the outcome, you can be assured of benefitting from that. Anyway, we weren't expecting to see you today, so why are you here?"

"I've got plenty of recording to catchup on," Colin replied almost glumly.

"Fine," Cora replied. "You can take it all home then and I'll look forward to seeing you tomorrow. You give me a proper debrief when you've had time to digest it all properly. Go on, get whatever you need and make yourself scarce."

"Thanks, Cora," Colin replied, now more energised. "I'll do just that, if you don't mind."

"See you tomorrow then, Colin," she said finally.

Updating case records at home proved to be a more effective means of setting interviews to one side than Colin might have imagined. He made considerable headway in finalising some short-term cases. At just turned 5.30pm, the phone rang. He guessed right. It was the familiar voice of a certain police woman who had not long completed an unusual 9-to-5 shift. "How did it go then, Colin?" Helen eagerly wanted to know.

"Well, I can't really say," he replied glibly. "They have been interviewing all day, including external candidates apparently. I did okay of sorts but, as anyone might say, it could have been better. It would make a big difference if I had the opportunity of answering some of those questions now".

"When will you know?" Helen asked.

"Sometime tomorrow, though that will be any time later on for the also-rans. It will depend on their first being able to secure the acceptance of an offer from the successful candidate."

"Right then, forget it for now. Put it right out of your mind," came an unflinching directive. "More important than any of that is the time you will be calling for *me*?"

"Er… let me think now…" Colin replied in an overly exaggerated way. "How about a week on Tuesday then?"

"Huh, forget it!" came the reply. "You'd better be here by half-seven or you'll be in big trouble."

"Yes, miss!" he replied, ringing off.

They spent another enjoyably relaxing evening that included a pleasant stroll to a quiet country pub. It provided a fitting haven, free from work, where Colin could share with Helen his uninhibited feelings about the interview. Moreover, in the company of the one true woman in his life, he was able to relegate career hopes and ambitions to more proportionate perspectives. While that still mattered to him, in the relative sanctity of such a tranquil setting, it certainly did not matter most. There were much more important things in his life.

The next morning found Colin arriving first in the office car park. He did not need his office keys though since the cleaners were still busy at work. He lodged the case files he had been working on at home, variously with typists or in Cora's tray. Then, of course, there were inevitably bits and pieces languishing expectantly in his pigeon-hole. He perused them accordingly as he wandered slowly upstairs to the Intake office. Thankfully, at this time of day, there would not even be a raucous Ivor Axford to tolerate. As he reached the landing, however, he noticed Cora's unmistakable maroon Austin Cambridge gliding into the car park below.

Having lodged various assortments on his desk, he made himself a cup of coffee. This would allow Cora time to get her feet notionally under her desk and, of course, to compulsorily *lightup*. It only then occurred to him, upon approaching her office, how he had not prepared in any way for the anticipated gist of his interview feedback. Never mind. He would simply tell it just how it was.

"Come on in, Colin," she hailed in response to his tap on the door. "Saw you were already in," she announced, partly hidden through a familiar plume of blue smoke. On this occasion though, he found this characteristic haze to be strangely welcoming. "Sit yourself down and give me a blow-by-blow account. Rumour has it that they were at it all day."

Colin's vague suspicions about Cora already having prior insider knowledge were soon dispelled. His would be her first glimmer of feedback and that in itself would be unusual in Colin's experience. He went on to repeat the interview account that he had already delivered on various other occasions. That encapsulated his performance as one of having been 'Okay in parts', and stressing how it could have been better.

Much of that overview was necessarily repeated during the course of the whole morning as various colleagues – including Elizabeth Winstanley – enquired with genuine interest. This extended to their wishing him the best. That said, Ivor had still not yet had the opportunity of posing his predictable two penn'orth. In spite of all that, Colin really had no alternative to just patiently remaining at his desk to await an increasingly nerve-wracking phone call.

Being quite unable to concentrate on anything really constructive that morning, he usefully busied himself on non-urgent catch-up tasks. These largely comprised of filing and simultaneously discarding superfluous accumulated material from desk drawers, so that the newly acquired space could soon be filled again. He still happened to be sorting that with Pam when Karen sang across the admin office, "May Overton on the phone for you, Colin!"

In spite of his having instilled in himself the need for a cool and collected response to this anticipated call, that undertaking immediately evaporated as Colin went distinctly weak at the knees. "Can you put it through to the interview room then please, Karen?" he asked in a mutedly flustered way that may not have been apparent to others.

"Hello-o-o," he said nonchalantly on lifting the receiver. He heaved a deep intake of breath.

"Colin?" the voice at the other end said enquiringly. "This doesn't seem a very clear line. It's May Overton here, Colin," she said in a slightly raised voice to make herself heard. "I'm really sorry about this delay in getting back to you about yesterday's interview. We've been somewhat held up by Mike Colburn having to deal with other pressing matters this morning."

"That's okay," he replied brightly, without any hint of pathos.

"Well, Colin, the thing is… well," Mrs Overton continued, "we'd like to offer you the senior social worker post at Chatterton."

He was speechless. "Are you there, Colin?" she asked again, in that slightly raised tone.

"I certainly am, May," he replied, before hurriedly adding. "Er… Mrs Overton, and I am really pleased to accept the offer."

"That's good then, Colin. Welcome aboard! I need you to make arrangements with my secretary, Andrea McKie, for your coming to see me sometime next week to finalise bits and pieces, like a starting date. Would that be okay?"

"It certainly would," said Colin. "Thank you very much."

"Congratulations then," the area officer said warmly. Colin vividly imagined that welcoming smile of hers that he'd found so encouraging at their last meeting in the interview. "I'll look forward to seeing you next week, then."

Colin repeated his grateful thanks before plonking himself down heavily on the chair by the interview room telephone. "Wo-ow!" he said audibly. "However will I begin to spread news of this?"

SEVENTEEN

Throws of the dice

COLIN TOOK A DEGREE of comfort from having prior knowledge of at least some of the Chatterton staff. He'd met several of them routinely during emergency duty shifts and in-service training events. Others, like Alwyn Timms, a senior colleague on one of Chatterton's long-term case management teams, he knew from social services football team's Sunday league exploits.

Much like Longley, there were seven staff on the Chatterton Intake team. They were comprised of a mixture of qualified and unqualified social workers, together with two social work assistants, who had considerable experience in allied fields. Colin considered it an impressive resource. Some of the qualified workers had acquired positive reputations of their own among the wider workforce. He could not really understand exactly why the team had endured such a fleeting sequence of senior social worker managers over recent years. They appeared to have had, so he mischievously thought, nearly as many managers as Aston Villa!

Chatterton was a not untypical industrial community. Pre-war relative prosperity had long since succumbed to the onset of urban decay, which brought with it familiar social pressures, aggravated by poverty, not just in terms of wealth, but also opportunity.

Becoming properly acquainted with new colleagues was hastened for Colin by the familiar shape of Intake workloads, typically extending to almost the full range of social work priorities. He drew heavily upon the fitting example set by Cora Malone's open-door access for staff. Concerns expressed on behalf of elderly people – and of others with physical disabilities – considerably exceeded the number of referrals received on behalf of children and families, or of people with mental health problems. Those proportions, however, often became reversed when it came to the required extent of worker input. The circumstances of children and their families would often be driven by uncompromising complexity.

One marked difference from Cora's fine example in the application of senior social work practice, was Colin's inclination to get his hands dirty, so to speak. He favoured the prospect of occasionally leading by example in effecting direct contact with clients. This was in spite of more experienced senior social workers – particularly those of Cora's 'old school' – cherishing marked distinctions in keeping separate the supervision and management of staff from direct intervention with clients.

Discovering therefore, that a particular member of the Chatterton Intake team, one Phill Vernon, was enrolled on the mental health course represented a particularly intriguing aspect of Colin's baptism in management. While Phill was an experienced practitioner, his qualifying background had been forged in the probation service. His relatively recent transfer to social services was perhaps a somewhat unusual direction of travel, but it was one that appealed to Phill's instincts towards social work horizons beyond criminal justice. His experience, fuelled by unwavering commitment to practice, was a real asset to the team.

Colin's early supervisory contact with Phill identified impending mental health course objectives. This sparked fond recollections of his own rewarding experiences under Tom Shone and inspired him to trade on Tom's fine example. They did not have to wait long before a likely opportunity came along. A request was accordingly received from a local GP for an assessment for the compulsory admission of a 45-year-old woman with a long history of psychiatric illness. Although Phill was not the named duty officer that day, he readily accepted the opportunity of accompanying Colin to undertake the necessary assessment.

Case records revealed that the patient, Judy Evans, was well-known to social workers in similarly acute circumstances. When her mental health was satisfactorily managed via medication, under the supervision of community nursing staff, Judy was able to function quite happily with the support of her husband and her seventeen-year-old daughter. For any number of less obvious reasons, however, her stability was prone to unanticipated disruption upon sudden phases of manic outbursts and the subsequent onset of self-neglect.

Setting necessary standards in highlighting best practice for Phill – when it was actually in the best interests of Mrs Evans – Colin rang the GP, Dr Logan, to request a joint visit. Dr Logan readily agreed – a far from guaranteed response among busy GPs – though he explained that the patient was better known to another partner.

Shouting and screaming were to be heard as Colin and Phill approached the front door of the terraced property. Poor Mrs Evans was plainly evident upon arrival: extremely unkempt, with evidence of singeing to her clothes, as she constantly paraded up and down, wringing her hands. Requests for her to perhaps take a seat and engage with the visitors went singularly unheeded. She was in perpetual motion. Dr Logan thankfully arrived soon afterwards.

Mr Evans remained remarkably detached throughout this unravelling episode, claiming to have been seeking assistance from the community nursing team for two weeks or more. He said his wife was eating and sleeping very little and, on this particular morning, her 'ranting and raving' had become aggravated to the point of being impervious to all attempts at distraction. Colin's inclination to stand back to allow Phill to take the lead in conducting necessary discussions was quite futile. There were few discussions to be had beyond acknowledging the pressing implications to stem this crisis. It was also abundantly clear that poor Mrs Evans was in no position to express any rationally informed opinion on the prospect of going to hospital.

Under these circumstances, the need for her compulsory admission was compelling. Hardly any astute social work interpretations were required. Dr Logan helpfully rang the duty psychiatrist, before confidently completing his necessary written medical recommendation as part of the process, before leaving subsequent arrangements to the social workers. Given the relative urgency of a well-known patient's circumstances, the duty psychiatrist wasted little time in conferring with Mrs Evans' consultant, Dr Senghal, before he also eventually arrived at the family home.

All of that inevitably took a considerable time. With Mr Evans remaining singularly detached, there was little else for the social workers to do beyond just being there, trying to support a couple under considerable duress. The duty psychiatrist – whose name Colin could not immediately decipher from his hurried introduction – similarly needed little time in confirming the diagnosis before accordingly completing the second medical recommendation. This was duly accompanied by the consultant's familiar expenses claim for Phill's endorsement. Such was the extent of Phill's intervention on that occasion.

The approved social worker application was otherwise for Colin's completion, as part of the necessary formalities. Mrs Evans was then transported to the psychiatric wing of the local hospital by ambulance, with the social workers following behind. Mr Evans remained at home. His being regarded – at the very least by his wife – as superfluous in these circumstances, was familiar territory. The admission thereafter became very straightforward. "There was little to learn from that," Colin subsequently remarked to Phill, "beyond appreciating how these formal processes should be conducted. I can assure you they're not always like that one."

Little did they know, however, that the opportunity of returning to the prospect of compulsory admissions would arise yet again that week. This second example conformed to Colin's earlier assertion that similar types of case have no obligation to mirror one another. This later one concerned Tony Stevens, a thirty-eight-year-old married man with two teenage sons, who again had a long psychiatric history. Mrs Stevens had contacted their GP to say that she could no longer cope with her husband's behaviour, though the nature of that behaviour was unspecified. The GP had accordingly contacted social services for an initial assessment. Having routinely noted past contacts on Mr Stevens's behalf, Colin and Phill duly made their way to his address, agreeing en route that Phill would take the lead.

The Stevens's home was a comfortably furnished council property where they were cordially received. Having explained the reason for their call as merely a request from the GP, it was not entirely clear whether Mr Stevens knew that it was his wife who had actually initiated this contact. She in turn, perhaps understandably, gave no inkling that this had been the case. Colin felt this uncertainty placed the social workers at some disadvantage in trying to embark upon honest exchanges. Beyond that, however, he could not eliminate the likelihood of Mrs Stevens probably having good reason for not mentioning it. Phill meanwhile stuck to the relatively passive tack of initial information-gathering.

Mr Stevens embarked upon a lucid account of family circumstances, speaking about his sons' likes and dislikes and of their progress at school. His younger son, Andrew, was a staunch West Bromwich Albion supporter. At length though, some of his ideas began to pose hints of paranoia as he dwelt uncompromisingly upon details of his wife's alleged infidelity some years previously with someone at work. For any unsuspecting third party, including the two social workers, there was of course no immediate way of knowing where the truth of all of that lay – or whether it was indeed the product of distorted thought processes. Stevens's own unashamed certainty of it was compounded by his belief that an eighteen-year-old receptionist at his own workplace was their illegitimate daughter. That child, so he believed, had taken the place of a child who he and his wife had lost postnatally, before their sons were born. Yet again, there was no immediate certainty of fact or otherwise.

Intermittently, he was verbally aggressive towards his wife, particularly when she was inclined to challenge some of his assertions. Phill then tried to steer the discussion more towards other aspects of here and now, by asking particularly about Tony's appetite, then about sleep patterns. While there was perhaps some evidence of his being depressed, his train of thought did not obviously appear to be unduly affected beyond specific details of family history to which he had referred. He spoke confidently about past phases of his own psychiatric history, including one episode of in-patient treatment following the death of his mother, then of his latest outpatient appointment with his consultant that had only taken place that morning. This was said to have led to adjustments being made to medication before he later returned to work.

For her part, Mrs Stevens found all this very trying. Close to the end of her tether, she attempted to play for the social workers tape-recordings of her husband's recent ravings, but which he managed to persist in prohibiting. She claimed that she feared for her safety following an episode of her husband pushing her, two days previously. She also confidently believed that he would very likely be sent home early from work on the following day. In the wake of it all, she was adamant about her intention to deny him access to the house on his returning home. As the interview spiralled increasingly into the couple's vitriolic exchanges, Colin and Phill swapped hurried glances, each searching some means of easing the tension and of simultaneously making sense of it in terms of assessment.

Colin abruptly took it upon himself to intervene. "None of this is getting us anywhere," he said sternly. He promptly added in an appreciably hushed tone, "Goodness knows what effect it will be having on your sons, let alone yourselves." This almost surprisingly had a measure of desired effect. The couple fell silent. With heads down, their self-consciousness was almost audible.

Colin seized on the opportunity of that fleeting silence. He repeated in a continuously hushed and kindly way, "This isn't getting any of us anywhere. Mr Stevens, you are still in the throes of getting used to a recent change in your medication regime. You have to take at least some responsibility in managing the effects of all of that, particularly for the sake of your family.

"Mrs Stevens, you clearly find your husband's behaviour very difficult at times and, from what we've seen, that's perfectly understandable. It may not, however, necessarily be a feature, nor indeed the product, of his illness on every occasion. Looking towards mental health services to provide solutions to matrimonial difficulties may not always be the answer. There may be other avenues to explore and we would be prepared to work with you in trying to find agreeable ways forward."

"Like what?" said Mrs Stevens with a frown. "What do you mean?"

"Well," Colin replied, desperately fearing he could be skating on thin ice here in terms of the state of their marriage, and simple truths about alleged infidelity. "We would be prepared to work with you as a family in identifying agreed objectives. These could seek to explore elements of shared objectives in managing your relationship, if that's what each of you want, or in exploring alternative options, whatever you may each consider them to be. We've not yet broached how or whether your two sons are affected by all this acrimony. Tony's mental health may only represent one part of the difficulties you describe." He was very conscious of potentially unresolved depths of grief surrounding the death of their first child. "I'm just saying that mental health services, and indeed the Mental Health Act itself, may not always be the best answer, that's all. What do you think?"

Tony remained silent, which Colin was inclined to regard as a welcome alternative to outbursts. "We'll see what tomorrow brings," Jane Stevens replied passively.

"My colleague here, Phill, will be in touch with you tomorrow then," Colin said, "if that's an agreeable way forward for now?" There was no reply. A faint smile by way of acknowledgement, otherwise avoiding eye contact, was the most that Jane Stevens could muster.

"What did you make of all that then, Phill?" Colin mused as they got into the car.

"Well," Phill replied, exhaling heavily, "I made it a shed-load of emotions and I'm not at all sure about which way it's going."

"Did you think Stevens was sectionable though?" Colin asked.

"Not necessarily," Phill surmised. "Nor am I even aware of hospital being put forward as an option, either by the GP or indeed the consultant who had, after all, only seen him this morning. While he seemed lucid enough in many respects, I fear we could well have turned our backs on a deteriorating situation."

"I agree," Colin confessed, "but is Mrs Stevens resorting solely to the Mental Health Act to solve other problems? Is it rather that her husband happens to have a convenient psychiatric label that routinely provides a handy solution? It could well be the state of their relationship that is the real problem, aggravated by mutual reluctance to do anything about it."

"Isn't that a case for marriage guidance then?" Phill pondered.

"Good point," Colin acknowledged, "except the mental health component may not have yet been eliminated." That said though, he did think that Phill had a fair point.

"Hmm…" mused Phill, "we'll have to see."

The final outcome, however, eventually came to pass upon yet another throw of the dice by the following morning. Melvin Allen, who had been on duty the previous evening, rang the duty officer at Chatterton, Gill Norwood, to say that Tony Stevens had been admitted to hospital under Section 2 of the Mental Health Act. Fractious family exchanges may have been waged later, alongside a revised cast of professionals, perhaps understandably leading to a somewhat different climax. All of that would certainly set the scene for revised scripts upon Phill's anticipated sequel.

It also generated a buzz among Intake team members as they gathered, at the allotted time, in Colin's office for their weekly allocation meeting. "Sounds something almost like a baptism of fire," Gill commented, on hearing extracts of Phill's finely balanced judgements about psychiatric admissions.

Those reflections were then interrupted when Mary Ewart and Barbara Isaacs entered the office. These particularly experienced and influential social workers were in the midst of discussing the circumstances of a fifteen-year-old girl, with whom they had each severally had involvement over recent months. It had subsequently transpired apparently, via Barbara's informal but finely tuned network, that the teenager concerned had more recently 'fallen pregnant'. This caused them to consider the extent to which females actually become pregnant.

"Mother's sister was always unequivocal about the likelihood of her niece getting pregnant," Mary announced confidently. "She was often heard to say that she was as randy as wild raspberries." That then, on their entering the team meeting, effectively ended an uncertain professional discussion.

Once Myra Jackson and Billy Lumsden had joined the gathering, with Emmie Quayle hurrying in last minute, the weekly allocation meeting was quorate. Colin opened the business by allowing Phill the opportunity of highlighting some of the professional ups and downs of two contrasting mental health assessments conducted that week. Not least of these, as Phill went on to explain, was news that morning of Colin's and Phill's original position on behalf of Tony Stevens being unwaveringly reversed, on the intervention of emergency-duty staff.

"That just goes to show," Barbara observed, "how any professional assessment, no matter how astutely it may have been put together, can be turned on its head by just one additional piece of information. That could be revealed on speaking to the social worker who made the application, Phill."

"The case perhaps also illustrates how marital discord and the onset of psychiatric symptoms are sometimes difficult to disentangle," Mary added. "It's similar," she said, "to the dilemma of managing distinctions between effectively supporting families collectively and of simultaneously evaluating emerging risks to any one or other individual family member." Some nodding in agreement failed to find anything constructive to add.

"On the matter of conflicting tensions though," Colin asserted, "is the evident upsurge in the diagnosis of child sexual abuse that has been reported in parts of north-east England." Barbara remarked how this recent trend appeared to have been linked to aspects of particular physical diagnosis in certain regional hospitals. "The matter of tensions though," Colin added, cheaply trying to maintain that theme, "is apparently extending to ways in which contributing agencies are able to work together in that part of the world. And that compatibility, of course, lies at the heart of our professional practice."

"Like mental health assessments," Phill observed, probably with Tony Stevens still on his mind.

Much of the remainder of the meeting was concerned with Colin allocating to individuals incoming cases received by the team during the previous week or so. Colin explained that Phill's quota would take account of his follow-up on each of the two mental health cases already acknowledged. A number of more straightforward referrals on behalf of elderly or disabled people requiring general support, including provision of disability aids and assessments for day care, were shared between Myra and Billy.

One of them was a referral for the provision of a telephone on behalf of someone with a defined disability. It represented a familiar request that had a reputation of its own among social work staff. Word had evidently got round local communities that this particular form of assistance was an explicit aspect of provision under the

Chronically Sick and Disabled Persons' Act. Less widely known, however, were the relatively strict criteria by which the local authority would even begin to consider assistance in providing telephones. This proverbial gap in understanding led to endless debate between locally elected members – on behalf of constituents – and social work staff, that remained endlessly difficult to bridge to any mutual degree of satisfaction.

There were consequently murmurs of muted cheering when Colin handed Myra the telephone request. "It's okay," she said. "I'm quite used to telling people what exactly they can't have." She was joking of course. Myra was otherwise well-used to these assessments, to very good effect.

Mary received two assessments for 'mothers' own adoption'. These were circumstances in which a parent – usually mothers – with custody of a child from a previous relationship, would apply to the County Court together with their current spouse for their joint custody of children from the original relationship. These applications were of course the subject of due process, including that of obtaining necessary consents, incorporated into a detailed social work assessment that the application was in the best interests of the children concerned. It was a process in which Mary had wide experience, earning her considerable esteem in the court arena.

Emmie Quayle, the youngest qualified social worker on the team, was allocated the case of a four-year-old child with whom her colleague, Gill Norwood, had become acquainted on a routine duty shift. The child had been seen in nursery school with severe bruising to the outside of her right thigh. Since it clearly raised certain suspicions among nursery staff, this led to Gill making contact with the child's mother and subsequently taking mother and child to hospital for the injury to be assessed. A paediatric examination had sought to establish its cause and an opportunity of potentially identifying any other injuries.

In the event, there was none. No explanation, however, could be given by mother nor child for the concerning bruise. The episode had otherwise highlighted the extent to which a twenty-one-year-old single parent might have been adequately coping with the inevitable demands of two young children. Their ground-floor flat was also somewhat distant from their wider family network. Emmie was therefore allocated this case to conduct a further assessment of family circumstances, including that of identifying likely scope for additional measures of support.

Gill Norwood and Barbara Isaacs thereafter shared the remaining handful of referrals for further intervention. Colin then confirmed forthcoming supervision slots already identified that week, together with the next allocation meeting – same time, same place – for the following week. Business was done.

EIGHTEEN

Epilogue

WORKING AT CHATTERTON DURING the late 1980s brought Colin Millwood a raft of new dimensions to his evolving career. Generally rewarding experiences were stimulated within a supportive office environment, blessed with apparently caring and committed colleagues on all three fieldwork teams. An added bonus coincided with the arrival, soon after Colin, of one Charlie Gerard. He was a colleague known to Colin from university days – and yet another member of Social Services FC to boot – who came to manage one of the other long-term teams. Even more fittingly, Colin considered Charlie an inspirational social worker, whose earlier life experiences had been forged in the east end of London.

The Intake team certainly conformed to the caring and committed stereotype, comprising of mutually supportive colleagues experienced in maintaining an effective duty system. At its core, so Colin thought, was a professional approach that clung steadfastly to its ability to relate spontaneously to ordinary people. While the essence of that appeared to be delivered in generally mild and non-officious ways, it clung diligently to acknowledged generic methodology for addressing wide-ranging social needs. Each individual team member traded on the wisdom of their own past professional experiences. Phill Vernon's, of course, had been in criminal justice, while Barbara Isaac's was in child guidance and Mary Ewart's in the broader field of education.

To what extent, however, such attributes were representative of the wider social work world was less clear. National headlines continued to be dominated by an unrelenting sequence of children who had died tragically at the hands of adult abusers. Then Colin's earlier veiled reference to apparently rising trends in cases of child sexual abuse in north-eastern England suddenly exploded into almost cataclysmic proportions. The non-metropolitan county of Cleveland had apparently become consumed by an unprecedented rise in cases of child sexual abuse during 1987. This had generated widespread concern, not just among the families concerned, but by health care staff, the police, MPs, the press and indeed the wider public.

The social and political turmoil that followed led to a formally constituted judicial inquiry into arrangements for dealing with suspected cases of child sexual abuse in that authority. It was led by the highly respected High Court judge, Elizabeth Butler-Sloss, who subsequently became a Dame Commander of the British Empire (DBE). What had initially arisen from paediatricians adopting a particular physical methodology in diagnosing sexual abuse had subsequently resulted in the removal of over a hundred children from their families.

The Report of the Inquiry into Child Abuse in Cleveland 1987 (HMSO 1988) was highly critical of an insipid lack of understanding between contributing agencies in such a critical area of work. That, in turn, had led to abjectly poor inter-agency communication. Paediatricians would apparently be inclined to reach firm conclusions about cases of suspected abuse referred to them. This had sometimes led to social workers implicitly complying with questionable medical opinion, devoid of any appreciable assessment of their own, before applying to courts for place of safety orders to remove children into care. Fundamental disagreements that may well have arisen in such cases between social workers and police officers were lamentably allowed to drift, unsurprisingly fuelling mutual mistrust. This thereby resulted in the police retreating from a multidisciplinary approach to work that had widely become the bedrock upon which its merits had been founded.

Lessons from Cleveland were enshrined in the inquiry's findings. These dwelt largely on an apparent mindset of unmitigated over-reaction to certain episodes of alleged abuse. This had arisen, of course, in the wake of a decade of alarming professional indifference being shamefully revealed throughout a host of child death inquiries nationally. While the notion of 'damned if you do and damned if you don't' may well have occurred to feckless observers, the challenge of rather finding ways of applying professional integrity to often finely balanced judgements had much more to commend it. Of 121 Cleveland children who were originally diagnosed as having been sexually abused, and promptly separated from their parents, only twenty-one had remained in care for at least some period of time.

Cleveland had famously sounded the clarion call in regarding children as individuals, not as 'objects of concern', urging social workers to listen carefully to what they had to say. This remarkably extended to having to articulate – indeed to the helping professions no less – about treating families with courtesy and respect! It also heralded the arrival of the term 'child protection' to professional discourse as an actively unbiased alternative to any familiar accusatory 'abusive' terminology. Moreover, the inquiry's findings led to substantial rewriting of the draft Children Act 1989 – the first major overhaul of childcare legislation in over forty years – that resulted in its delayed implementation until October 1991.

As illuminating as all this was for Colin's evolving management perspective, in throwing down a gauntlet to make real differences for families, it served only to heap upon him more acute despondency when the harrowing events surrounding little Stephanie Finch eventually reached the popular press. While much of the thinking driven by Cleveland had revealed new professional horizons, Colin seldom contemplated any new initiative without trying to imagine what difference it could have possibly made for her. Even the expressed support within the local media of the chairman of social services about social work services to Stephanie's family failed to allay Colin's enduring misgivings about her tragic fate.

The new Children Act embraced wide-ranging considerations in working towards what it fervently regarded as its 'paramount' objective of promoting a child's welfare. Principles were founded upon the notion that, while children are best cared for within their own families, the corresponding legal rights and responsibilities of parenthood were otherwise made clear. Legislation extended to defining what it saw as 'children in need', focusing on identifying particular additional needs an individual child may have to effectively promote their welfare. Those sorts of needs could arise for any number of conspiring reasons, including an aspect of disability or indeed from any inclination towards criminal behaviour.

It incorporated wider understanding of fostering and adoption within a range of measures in looking after someone else's child, including a member of one's own family. All-encompassing elements of the legislation extended to the newly defined notion of significant harm, and of local authorities' duty to investigate circumstances whereby a child was likely to suffer harm. Notably in the wake of Cleveland, the fundamental contribution of the police towards safeguarding priorities was explicitly emphasised.

Preparations for the advent of such an influential piece of legislation became a major undertaking for local authorities. Widespread ''89-Act' training represented a national priority, as professional agencies simultaneously worked hard to maintain unrelenting day-to-day services. Acquiring more innovative practice considerably enriched emerging professionalism, occasionally reflected in evolving terminology. 'Clients' became 'service users' in dispensing with any dubious misunderstanding about the personal integrity of people accessing social care. Such subtle nuances in terminology sometimes caused Charlie Gerard to query the basis for pupils in schools somehow acquiring the 'students' label. It became a familiar theme, later extending to his doubting whether schools acquiring 'academy' status had actually procured any additional capability to ensure academic success.

More seriously, however, promoting effective means of facilitating social workers' ability to talk effectively to parents about child welfare concerns became a compelling feature of this new dawn. It was notably reminiscent of Cora Malone's familiar challenge for staff in being equipped to 'talk to an angry man' about the care of his children. This became reinforced via the gathering momentum to appreciate the negative potential of drug and alcohol abuse upon 'good enough' parenting. Such wayward intrusions into family life regrettably have capacity for further compromise when domestic violence brings additional havoc to family circumstances.

New challenges, of course, were not simply confined to work with children and families. More demanding appreciation of adults' social care needs became pressing in other sectors. Assessing older people effectively for community support, among other care provision, similarly became the source of new legislation. It brought revised organisational structures to embryonic concepts of 'provider' services and indeed to the relative means of funding care and treatment.

Changes inevitably extended to transitions in mental health legislation and practice. The concept of an approved mental health professional replaced the singular role previously confined to that of the approved social worker. A later statutory amendment brought other experienced mental health care professionals, like nurses and occupational therapists, into the critical role of assessing patients for compulsory admission or detention under the Mental Health Act 1983.

It was hardly surprising that in this mindset of innovation and change – and ever increasing public expectations of professional expertise in social care settings – that the shortcomings of generic social work practice were finally laid bare. The case for local authority social work departments to look towards the segregation of adult services provision from work with children and families, sought to keep pace with evolving research and development. Expectations seemed to eclipse demands for professional integrity, to the point of expertise rather becoming the product of natural progression.

This inevitably brought considerable investment in research into work with children and families. It focused intently on stimulating preventative notions of 'child protection' as distinct from the reactive mind-set of addressing 'child abuse'. Appreciating those crucial differences within family environments could sometimes become glibly misconceived. They were discouragingly articulated by some as simply advocating *a lighter touch*; by others to the unbelievable misconception of needing to *keep adults safe* from damning accusations about abusing children.

Listening carefully to what people had to say about their family life certainly remained a good beginning in understanding it. There was, however, a host of other prompts – verbal and non-verbal – about social workers acquiring measures of confidence in forming more reliable judgments about family dynamics and effective parenting. Working more efficiently with other people – professional and indeed non-professional – was just one telling case in point.

Welcoming strategic change, of course, was never in itself going to transform how lovingly children are cared for, nor in averting the advent of family tragedy. In a neighbouring authority, not far in fact from the Chatterton district office, the decomposing bodies of two newlyborn twins were found in a derelict house close to a town centre. Elsewhere in that same authority, ten-week-old Daniel died at the hands of his father, who was later jailed for manslaughter.

Perhaps even more remarkably, in the wake of Cleveland, came news of up to nine children being removed from their homes by social workers and police on the island of South Ronaldsay in Orkney. The subsequent formal Inquiry into the Removal of Children from Orkney 1991, chaired by Lord Clyde (UK Govt., Scottish Office) examined familiar allegations of child abuse, fuelled this time by a young girl's claim about ritualistic satanic abuse

– a phenomenon that had remarkably gained momentum elsewhere around that time.

Those allegations, however, were denied by all of the children allegedly concerned and neither were they substantiated on medical examination. When matters subsequently came to court, the presiding judge dismissed the local authority's case as fatally flawed, criticising social workers for what he clearly saw as incompetence. The Churchillian notion of guaranteeing how success might be achieved "by going from failure to failure with enthusiasm", had somehow struck a damning chord.

Colin was indeed mindful of how such lurid episodes, often determined simply by tragedy or merely on making headline news, travelled fast. In other respects, routine episodes of adequately provided social care, let alone those bringing welcome changes to peoples' lives, somehow had much less to commend them. Looking back, the appreciation of those who Colin remembered expressing such grateful thanks for their holiday in Skegness, or the clinging embrace of Gemma Graham and her mother in a daunting city police station, would never hit the headlines.

He was at least able to share, albeit at third hand, events of more agreeable upturn in family life when supervising the work of his colleagues. Mary's considerable expertise in the field of 'mothers' own' adoption was lamentably difficult to celebrate beyond the warm commendations of grateful families outside court. Similarly, Barbara's experience in child and adolescent mental health was of considerable advantage when negotiating access to specialist health care networks that generated such appreciable differences in the lives of some young people.

Bad news though is seldom far away. The abduction of a two-year-old child by two ten-year-olds from a shopping centre in Liverpool had hit the headlines well before his mutilated body was found on a railway line two days later. The public outcry that followed had generated fiercely contrasting opinions about what needed to be done. They ranged between demands for the profiles of those involved to be made known, while others lamented the unlikely prospect of beginning to apply any agreeable means of criminal justice to such young offenders. Such fundamentally opposing views fuelled heated debates that have never completely abated, even now, and certainly not in Liverpool.

But headline atrocities may not be confined to violent child deaths. The widely acclaimed personable qualities and charitable fundraising of the TV celebrity, Jimmy Savile, only became unequivocally called into serious question in the wake of his death. Extensive media coverage and multiple witness statements subsequently revealed an extremely different emerging profile of someone that otherwise had haplessly fallen short of any judicial analysis.

Indeed, lessons from history remain vivid impressions upon the integrity of wisdom. Contributing professional agencies have since come together to work much more effectively in 'hubs'. Beyond all that, however, nothing will quite dispel the harsh reality of Robert Burns' solemn declaration of 'man's inhumanity to man'. Neither can such perilous blind spots, forged by all manner of distractions, ever be eradicated from unimaginable depths of social despair.

 **Matador**